Marco Hunter

Signed copy!

May sunshine light your way.

James P. Leynse

BY THE SAME AUTHOR

PRECEDING THE MAYFLOWER
(The Pilgrims in England and
in the Netherlands)

WIVES ARE BUT LEAVES
(Chinese concubine system)

THE LURE
(Chinese legends)

YOU CAN'T CLAP WITH ONE HAND
(Communist infiltration of China)

FREEDOM'S GATEWAY
(The struggle of a Chinese
against old-fashioned parents)

THE TWAIN SHALL MEET
(A Chinese student's battle
against old superstitions)

PRECEDING
THE
MAYFLOWER

The Pilgrims in England
and
in the Netherlands

PRECEDING
THE
MAYFLOWER

The Pilgrims in England
and
in the Netherlands

BY

James P. Leynse

WITH AN INTRODUCTION BY

FRANCES DIANE ROBOTTI

Author and Historian on Early New England

 FOUNTAINHEAD PUBLISHERS, INC.
475 FIFTH AVENUE, NEW YORK, N.Y. 10017

AUTHOR'S ACKNOWLEDGMENTS

The inspiration compelling me to write this book was created by my friends of Pilgrim Place, Claremont, California for which I am deeply appreciative. I am also grateful for the cooperation of the staff of the libraries I visited in America and abroad, and the authors of the diverse publications I consulted.

I especially esteem the constant interest and enthusiasm in my manuscript shown by my wife, the wise and most efficient counsel of my Editor Frances Diane Robotti so unstintingly given, and the high skill of my publisher Rose P. Portugal. My debts and thanks are particularly due to Fountainhead Publishers for their unwavering faith in my book.

LOVINGLY DEDICATED

To my sister Francina

"They knew they were pilgrims and lifted their eyes to heaven, their dearest country and it quieted their spirits."

William Bradford's
History of Plimoth Plantation

"They were strangers and pilgrims on the earth."

Hebrews 9:13

CONTENTS

ABOUT THE AUTHOR

Born in Middelburg, Rev. James P. Leynse, studied in the Netherlands for the ministry. Later he took his graduate work at Princeton Seminary and was ordained in the Fifth Avenue Presbyterian Church of New York City. He and Mrs. Leynse went out to Peking, China, under the auspices of the United Presbyterian Board of Foreign Missions of America. For 26 years, the author was Pastor of the Chinese Presbyterian Church of Peking, doing all of his work in the Mandarin Chinese language.

According to British custom, Easter was celebrated on Sunday and Monday when he preached for the staff and soldiers of the different legations in English, Dutch, German and Chinese. He also speaks Flemish and understands French. For some time he served as Chaplain of the Chinese Army of General Feng Yu Hsiang.

Through the Dutch Embassy, Reverend and Mrs. Leynse were presented to P'u Yi, the last Emperor of China and were invited to his wedding dinner. Thereafter for four years, every Wednesday morning, Mrs. Leynse held a Bible class in their home for the ladies of the Court, who were still allowed to live in the Forbidden City.

From 1941 to 1943, during World War II, the Leynses were placed under house arrest by the Japanese military forces occupying China. From 1943 to 1945, they were interned in the British Embassy of Peking. He was elected Chaplain of their group and held regular services in the Embassy Chapel in the form and tradition of the Anglican Church, new to him as a Presbyterian minister. Rescued by the United States Marines, the Leynses found their belongings had been sequestered by the elders of the church. In 1946, they were expelled from China by the Communists. Rev. Leynse began writing his books on China during his imprisonment.

The years of privation in internment affected his health so drastically, he was declared disabled, so they returned from the Orient directly to Pilgrim Place in Claremont, California. Now they are both American citizens.

Born in Holland, Anna Maria Arnoldina Groenendyk (for practical reasons the family has dropped the traditional Rippertz Van), Mrs. Leynse joined her husband in missionary work, contributing full time to work among the women of Peking. Fluent in five languages (Dutch, English, French, German and Chinese), Mrs. Leynse did her college work in French at the University of Lausanne, Switzerland. Their two sons, Humphrey William and Waldo Henry, were educated in the Peking American School, completing their education in Switzerland and in Holland. Both graduated from Pomona College, Claremont, followed by graduate work at Stanford University. Entering the United States Foreign Service, both of Rev. Leynse's sons served twenty years in the Orient with the State Department. Humphrey is a film producer specializing in the Far East. He and his wife, the former Judith Light, teach at Washington State University. Their children comprise a daughter Anna Lei, a freshman college student, and her two small brothers of five and three. The second son called Wally, married to the former Ruth Wilson, is at Los Altos, California, specializing in land development, their daughter of eight is Terri.

An ancestor of Mrs. Leynse's was Lord Mayor of Leyden during the eleven years from 1609 to 1620 the Pilgrims spent there. It was, in fact, Johan Rippets-van Groenendyk, who invited the Englishmen to come to Leyden and who proved to be a close friend to them during their stay.

The Leynses live in their Mediterranean-style home in Pilgrim Place, full of the fascinating Oriental treasures they have collected from their very amazing life. Pilgrim Place is a community of retired professional Christian workers such as professors, college presidents, teachers, doctors, etc. a cooperative organization. The 310 Pilgrims occupy a little park with 130 small and large homes surrounded by gardens. Rev. Leynse's sister, Francina, widow of Dr. Edward Gaylord, occupies one of them. Members of this unusual group have been active in 18 countries and can converse in 21 different languages. There are 17 descendants of the *Mayflower* now living at Pilgrim Place: Dr. Charlotte De Forest, Mrs. Telford Erickson, Miss Lucia E. Lyons, Dr. Isabelle MacCausland, Miss Clara M. Standish, Mrs. Ellen Richardson, Mrs. Edward A. Steiner, Mrs. Ralph Trine, Dr. Williston Wirt, John Alden, Richard Warren, William Bradford, Myles Standish, William Brewster, Francis Cooke, William Bradford, Phil Osborne.

Inspired by his many years in the East, Rev. Leynse is now working on his next book to be entitled *China Tales*.

INTRODUCTION

This is the fascinating story of the small English group of Pilgrims, known as Separatists, who in Queen Elizabeth's time were driven by religious persecution from their homes in Scrooby to the Netherlands. It covers their sojourn there, the decision to leave for America, the turbulent negotiations and preparations for passage, the purchase of the *Speedwell* and hiring of the *Mayflower*, the passenger list, and eventual landing after a perilous winter Atlantic crossing as the *Mayflower* dropped anchor at Long Point in Provincetown Harbor, Cape Cod.

Reverend Leynse was born in Middelburg in the Netherlands. An ancestor of his wife, Johan Rippets-van Groenendyk, was elected eleven times Lord Mayor of the City of Leyden. It was, in fact, upon his invitation and direction that the Pilgrims settled in Leyden and lived for some ten years in that famous city.

Familiar with his native Dutch customs, places and events, he has skillfully interpreted the conditions to which the refugee Englishmen were exposed in the late 16th and early 17th centuries.

Preceding the Mayflower is a unique contribution to the ever-growing literature on the beginnings of New England. Conventional history teaching often unfairly implants an impression that the passengers of the *Mayflower* were the first English or other Europeans to come to New England, but

11

Plymouth Harbor had actually been entered six times before 1620, and it was Captain John Smith who widely advertised the commercial advantages of American colonization, sending back a shipload of sample cod in 1614, which brought a high price in Europe.

In his Preface, the author has wisely outlined the most important voyages to these shores by various adventurers, explorers and entrepreneurs, thus emphasizing the important truth that the first permanent settlement in New England actually began with the passengers of the *Mayflower* in 1620, and that *not* commerce but religion was the basic motive eventuating in the several commonwealths within New England. By intermarrying with the Puritans who flooded into Massachusetts Bay a decade later, to found Salem in 1628 and Boston in 1630 as well as other settlements, the descendants of the scant one hundred people who came over on the *Mayflower* grew into a present-day multitude of bona fide progeny.

The voyages which followed the *Mayflower* were organized by Puritans of education and reputation, a prosperous body of the English nation, consciously directed to founding on this continent a Puritan State with liberty of conscience. This book clarifies the difference between the Pilgrims, who were Separatists from the Anglican Prayer Book, the Queen Elizabeth Episcopacy and all national churches, and the Puritans, who believed in the union of Church and State. It reveals how the Pilgrims formed that essential link in the chain of events which led to the founding of Massachusetts Bay Colony by the Puritans of England. The group from Scrooby was compelled to separation. Refusing to conform, they had to flee for their lives, making their way to Holland, where freedom of religion was recognized. There they could establish themselves in a church of their own, joining with other groups of English dissenters. They established homes there, married, had children and became citizens in order to join the guilds and secure more skilled positions, but stopping just short of permanent settlement.

In his inimitable style, the author has conceived of his historical characters as people he might have known in familiar surroundings. Therefore his use of imagined but appropriate dialogue adds materially to the human dimension. A Presbyterian minister, the Rev. Leynse comes to his task with an insight fostered by his varied background, which includes 26 years as a pilgrim or stranger in his role as foreign missionary in China. Learning the Chinese language and absorbing the mysteries of an ancient land, he preached and taught, and survived a four-year war imprisonment at the hands of the Japanese.

We are fortunate to have a narrator whose contribution bears the stamp of originality combined with intimate knowledge of that important but neglected chapter in the lives of the Plymouth people prior to 1620. He has not spared himself in researching those bits of history which illuminate the joys and sorrows of a small group of courageous human beings. They suffered much, but, like Job, never swerved from worship of the God in whom they put their faith, while exercising every possible effort to better their situation.

Especially at this time of world-wide confusion, it is apropos to reconsider the humility and wisdom of these people in face of insuperable obstacles. As a minister himself, the author ably illustrates how these Christians made the best of the good things offered them as gifts of God, and how they endured hardships though not without many tears. He shows how much they depended on their Bible and its practical teachings, such as Psalm 133, "Behold how good and how pleasant it is for brethren to dwell together in unity," and Ecclesiastes 4, Verses 9 and 10, "Two are better than one because they have a good reward of their labor for if they fall, one will lift up his fellow and woe to him who is alone when he falls and has not another to lift him up."

The Pilgrims asked for honesty, disdained facade, pretenses and sham, fostered freedom of the mind. They may have had their contradictions and inconsistencies, but never forgot that man's whole duty is to revere God and keep His commandments. This is the theme which runs consistently throughout the book.

The Rev. Leynse's book epitomizes the value of sustaining family love, loyalty and kindness in a harsh world. The Pilgrims came from a small town in rural England where they traditionally thanked God for their daily blessings; they made new friends in Holland, but did not lose sight of their original ideals or religion and what they dreamed of as a better life for their children. Through the mires of poverty, sickness and multiple death, they never stooped to cynicism or bitterness.

While the author uses the term "Pilgrim" for its facility, he is aware that "forefather" would be more correct technically, since the word "Pilgrim" did not come into common use until 1840. William Bradford, who was himself a passenger on the *Mayflower*, wrote that "they knew they were pilgrims" in the sense of wanderers. This narrative is greatly enriched by the author's use of the remarkable document penned by Governor Bradford in his declining years. He had no thought of publication, simply the urge to record all that he could remember of people and events. Upon his death, it was entrusted to his son, Major William Bradford, who left it to his own son, Major John Bradford. Then it passed into the care of Judge Samuel Sewall of Boston. After Thomas Prince excerpted what he wanted from its pages, he put the volume on the shelves of his library in the steeple of the Old South Church in Boston. There it remained for at least half a century, as we know it was consulted in 1774 by Thomas Hutchinson, soon to flee the country as a Tory. When the Church was taken over by the British in the Revolution, and the library looted, the Bradford manuscripts disappeared.

Not until 1855 was the 270-page manuscript found, in the library in Fulham Palace on the outskirts of London. The search was directed there by a reference clue in a published book. The following year, it was a major literary event when *The History of Plimoth Plantation* by Governor William Bradford was published in Boston, Massachusetts, and for the first time the personal lives of the Pilgrims were brought into focus for the world to see. Fighting, talking, writing, bargaining or loving, these are an articulate people, sensitive yet lusty, well aware of the pleasures of this earth, and united in their crusade for freedom of worship.

The Rev. Leynse explains how the failure of the *Speedwell* was the chief cause of the interminable delays which brought the *Mayflower* to the shores of Massachusetts in the midst of a bitter winter. The arrivals were unable to provide adequate shelter for themselves, weakened as they were by scurvy and other illnesses, so that half their number came to untimely deaths. Yet, the next spring the survivors stood on the hills of Plymouth and watched as the *Mayflower* sailed for Old England, never to return to New England.

It is symbolic that the *Mayflower* should disembark its passengers, not in Northern Virginia or on the Jersey coast, but on Cape Cod, a section of the Atlantic coast so dreaded by mariners that the early Dutch and French called it Cape Malabarre (Bad Bar) for the numerous shipwrecks there. Summer visitors to the Cape simply cannot imagine the severity of the winter storms on this portion of the coast. Along the 40 miles of the Cape's dangerous Back Side on the Atlantic shoreline, millions of dollars' worth of treasure and thousands of lives have been swallowed up by the angry sea. In the 24 years from 1873 to 1897, one old record tells of 151 vessels being lost.

Mayflower was not an unusual name, for there were 20 vessels so named in service in 1620. In Plymouth, Massachusetts, a full-scale reconstructed *Mayflower*, which Captain Alan Villiers sailed to America from England in May of 1957, is on permanent display. The finest model ever executed of this famous vessel, exhibited in Pilgrim Hall, Plymouth, is by R. C. Anderson of Basset Holt, Southampton, England, Vice President of the Society of Nautical Research.

The best book on the nautical aspects of the *Mayflower* is W. Sears Nickerson's *Land-Ho!—— 1620.* This is a seaman's story of the *Mayflower*, her construction, her navigation and her landfall, with drawings by the author of deck plans, sail plans and passenger quarters, plus a map of Cape Cod, showing the *Mayflower*'s course as plotted by Captain Nickerson.

The Rev. Leynse's very timely book adds much of interest to the Pilgrim story, once more highlighted in 1970, as in 1920, on the 350th anniversary of their great adventure into the unknown. Again the searchlight of history shines on that small and feeble undertaking, glorified by faith, hope and charity, but necessarily limited by the slender resources of the poor and humble men who originated it.

In Holland, the Pilgrim exodus is commemorated with a full slate of events. In Leyden, where they settled for many years after a brief stay in Amsterdam, family mementoes, records and archives are on display at the town's Pilgrim Museum, with special lighting of historic buildings as Leyden re-enacts the circumstances of the Englishmen who settled in that town. On August 1, 1970, dignitaries from the United States and the Netherlands attended celebrations featuring the Pilgrims' departure from Leyden for Delftshaven, re-enacted by Leyden University students in 17th-century costumes, the festivities climaxing on November 26, 1970, Thanksgiving Day, with special services in honor of the Pilgrims at Pieterskerk, St. Peter's, Leyden, where the Rev. John Robinson is buried. A right-hand turn up the Breestraat, the narrow bustling street that forms the backbone of the old city, leads uphill to the imposing mass of that old church. Services were attended by

some Society of Mayflower Descendants and by American
servicemen.

In Amsterdam, a 20-year restoration program has been
inaugurated for 100 old buildings in the Port of Delftshaven,
from which the Pilgrims sailed for England in the *Speedwell*
to meet the *Mayflower* for the voyage to the New World.
Holland's Director of Tourism, Joop Strijkers, has hailed the
350th anniversary as an opportunity for his country to join
with Great Britain in inviting Americans to retrace their heritage
on the European side of the Atlantic. In this vein, British Overseas Airways highlighted Mayflower Year with a special tour to
bring modern-day Pilgrims to the Old Manor House in Scrooby,
England, where William Brewster, William Bradford and Pastor
Richard Clyfton organized the departure to Holland, while in
Plymouth, England, historical ships are exhibited along with a
1620 model town.

Preceding the Mayflower by the Rev. James P. Leynse
deserves the fairest of voyages, and should be of inestimable
value to all interested in probing the significant but neglected
European background of American colonization. It constitutes
a helpful short-cut to a great deal of factual material not easily
researched, indispensable to libraries, schools, colleges, and
historical and genealogical societies.

As with all literary undertakings so wide in scope, there
will be those who feel something of interest has been omitted,
or who will disagree with what has been included. For any such
differences, we plead forbearance, while proudly introducing
this truly admirable presentation by a sincere and able author.

New York City, New York   Frances Diane Robotti
July 22, 1971   Author and Historian
                                                          on Early New England

AUTHOR'S PREFACE

It seemed incredible to most colonials planning to emigrate to the New World in the 17th century that America had previously been explored, mapped and settled by a variety of other people who preceded them. For some time the group of Pilgrims who were to leave Leyden, Holland, in 1620, clung to the idea that they had been divinely destined to be the first settlers of the northern part of this continent. Yet as early as the 8th century, Vikings sailed westward from the Baltic and North Seas and in the 9th century they colonized Iceland.

In the year 986, the Norse navigator Herjuffson sailed from Iceland to Greenland, and when caught up in a storm, his vessel drifted on to Newfoundland and Labrador, but did not land, dreading cannibals. Between 1000 and 1008, Leif Erickson, son of Eric Thorvaldson, and his Norsemen from Greenland visited the North American coast. Leif landed in Labrador where he found the country pleasantly different from the cliffs of Greenland, the coast low and abounding in forests. Impelled by a spirit of adventure, he made a number of explorations as far south as Massachusetts, it is said, and remained there for a year. He may have visited Rhode Island and even found his way into the harbor of New York. When he and his sailors returned home, they were filled with tales of the newly discovered country. As a result, a number of Norwegian mariners came to these shores during the following year.

Norse legends tell us that in the year 1002, Leif's brother

Thorwald sailed as far as Maine and Massachusetts. He is known in Norway as the first white man to die in America; he was buried in what is now Fall River, Massachusetts. In 1005 another brother of Leif, Thorstein, landed here with a group of men, but did not stay. However, in 1007, Thorfinn Karlsefur arrived with one hundred and sixty people, as far as is known the first attempt to settle in America. The adventurers sailed in three ships with livestock aboard.

According to the legends, they explored the coast of Massachusetts, went as far south as Virginia, where they found wild corn and berries, and traded pieces of red cloth to the friendly natives for valuable furs. They are said to have stayed in Virginia throughout the winter, surprised by the mildness of the weather. It was a promising beginning, especially since Thorfinn's wife bore him a son named Snorri, the first white child in America.

Troubles began when the Norsemen drove harder bargains, offering less cloth and in other ways offending the Indians, whose friendliness changed to sullenness. They also contracted the diseases of the white men. The Indians landed their canoes when a fierce bull belonging to Thorfinn ran out of the forest and bellowed at the redmen, who fled in panic, only to return in a belligerent mood the moment their courage was restored. In the ensuing struggle a number of men were killed on both sides. Norwegian storytellers have it that Thorfinn's bull ended the attempt at a first settlement in America, as the white men left shortly afterwards.

Other companies of Norwegians and Icelanders followed unsuccessfully to the New World. Their chroniclers noted that it was a beautiful country, far better than their own frozen island of the north, but that they found too little to buy and sell to make their stay profitable. The Welshman Mardoch Owen voyaged to America in 1170, and during the 12th, 13th and 14th centuries, Norwegians continued voyaging to this hemisphere, but then the new country, called Vinland, was gradually forgotten. Historians, too, neglected the discovery. Europeans then lived in a Mediterranean-centered world, with the Crusaders trying to rescue the Holy Land from infidels. Christopher Columbus was ultimately destined to bring the New World to the attention of Europe.

On Friday, August 3, 1492, Columbus set sail from Palos, Spain, with his three vessels, *Nina, Pinta* and *Santa Maria*, and brought them to anchor on October 12 at the Bahama Island of Guanahani. He noted in his journal that the "naked inhabitants swarmed around our ships and gazed at the sailors as though we had come from heaven." They remained until January 16, 1493, then returned to Lisbon. Spain quickly claimed the land and asked recognition of the Pope. In September 1493, she sent forth an expedition of seventeen ships carrying fifteen hundred colonists to establish sovereign Spanish rights.

The exploits of Columbus, however, attracted little attention in Europe where communication of news was limited and many people were illiterate. But when the British Ambassador in Spain wrote to King Henry VII about Columbus, it aroused the monarch's interest: new lands could be had for nothing simply by sending emissaries to claim them officially. His advisors found just the man for him: John Cabot, an Italian navigator in his youth, now a wealthy merchant living in Bristol. Commissioned by Henry VII, he sailed from Bristol with five ships in April 1497, accompanied by his three sons, and found Cape Breton Island and Nova Scotia, taking possession in the name of England of all land from Labrador to Florida. It was considered of such little importance that he was rewarded by a gift of only Ł10 by the king. His son Sebastian sailed again in the spring of 1498, aiming for a northwest passage to the Indies like the explorers before him, but at Greenland, icebergs compelled him to change his course.

Sebastian Cabot explored the coastlines of Newfoundland, Nova Scotia and New England. He returned to England after reaching Cape Hatteras. In August 1498, Columbus sailed on his third voyage and reached the mouth of the Orinoco. Meanwhile Cabot made many voyages for Spain. The Pope honored the claims of the Catholic Spanish by drawing a north-south line 300 miles west of the Azores, giving the entire world west of that line to Spain. This infuriated Henry VII, but he dared not oppose the Pope. For a while his son and successor, Henry VIII, adopted the same policy, but after the Reformation began, he refused to take any further note of the papal decision.

Great social forces worked for five hundred years to transform Europe from feudalism into a modern world. In the 10th century the arts were little cultivated; cities were in decay or obliterated, and each town was self-sufficient. In the economic revival of the 11th century, trade between Europe and Africa and the East increased as barter gave way to a money economy; the Crusades helped break the barriers of isolation, and travelers' tales ever widened the known world. Marco Polo's journey to the Orient fired the imagination of Europeans in the 13th century. Medieval Europe in the 11th century had developed a thriving trade with Tripoli, Ceuta and other North African ports.

Portugal was a leader in exploration, with Bartholomew Diaz rounding the Cape of Good Hope in 1488. The long-sought passageway to the East was found ten years later when Vasco da Gama anchored his fleet at Calicut on the southwest coast of India, and the Spice Islands were discovered in the heart of the East Indies.

At the beginning of the 16th century, France awoke to its opportunities in the New World. In 1506 a Frenchman drew a map of the Gulf of St. Lawrence, but not until the 17th century were substantial French explorations undertaken in the New World. In 1512 Juan Ponce de Leon landed in Florida, which he named for the beauty of the tropical flowers he found. Ponce de Leon was wounded in a skirmish with the Indians and brought to Cuba to die, but his settlement on the site of St. Augustine remained. A year later, the governor,

Vasco Nunez de Balboa, learned from the natives of another ocean, which lay to the west. Crossing the Isthmus of Panama, Balboa came upon the peaceful body of water and named it the Pacific.

Explorations and claims continued. Spain sent out an expedition in 1519 under Fernando Cortez, who landed his fleet at Tabasco and began the conquest of Mexico, proceeding as far west as Vera Cruz where he was met by a delegation of the Emperor Montezuma. The Indians tried to dissuade Cortez from seeing the Emperor, but, undaunted, he marched with his Spanish soldiers toward the capital, then entered the city, amazed to find it gleaming with spires, temples and imposing buildings. The Spaniards camped in the central square near the temple of Aztec, the God of War, and remained for a month. They were thrilled to find great stores of silver and gold. Realizing the hostility of the natives, Cortez decided to take Montezuma prisoner and so gain control of the rich country. He coerced the sovereign to pay a huge fine of over six million dollars and provide a large annual tribute as a vassal of the King of Spain.

Before the Mexicans could revolt, the Spaniards attacked them as they celebrated a festival, killing five hundred including priests and leaders. In retaliation, the Mexicans laid seige to the Spanish garrisons. When Cortez felt in danger of being overwhelmed, he forced the Emperor to address his people from the top of his palace and order them to make peace. Listening in silent amazement, the enraged populace suddenly broke into a fury. Javelins sailed through the air, the ruler was struck, and fell fatally wounded by his own subjects. After his death, the Mexicans fought fiercely and Cortez and his army had to flee the city they had so long occupied by force of arms. But he returned with fresh troops and laid seige to the city for nine months until it fell. The dynasty of Montezuma was overthrown and Mexico became a Spanish province.

Not to be outdone by the success of Spain, France in 1524

tried again to get its share of the New World, placing Giovanni da Verrazano of Florence in charge of an expedition of four ships, three of which had to return to port in a heavy January storm. The *Dolphin* sailed alone and reached the shore of present Wilmington, Delaware. A sailor who had fallen overboard and was treated kindly by the Indians induced Verrazano to trade with the natives. Sailing north, he entered New York's harbor and bartered with the Indians there.

France in 1534 sent out Captain Jacques Cartier, a mariner of St. Malo, who reached Gaspé Bay and the St. Lawrence River in Canada and took possession for France. He later claimed the site of Montreal, but early attempts at settlement ended in failure. In 1541 five ships sailed to New France, but were unable to establish a permament colony.

The Protestant Admiral of France, Cologni, persuaded King Charles IX that he could best plant a colony in America through the Huguenots. This would serve two purposes: France would rid herself of these troublesome Protestants, and at the same time claim land in the area of Florida where this sect desired to settle. The Huguenots in essence were Separatists or Reformers, French Protestants dissatisfied with the authority and ritual of the Catholic Church. They aimed to build a colony somewhere with their own government and church while remaining French subjects just as the later Pilgrims remained British in feeling.

In February 1562, a large group of Huguenots sailed with Captain John Ribault. A number of released prisoners augmented the passengers, volunteering to assist in return for their freedom. Reaching the coast of America, they erected a fort at Port Royal and named the area Carolina in honor of Charles IX. Captain Ribault returned to France for additional supplies, leaving 26 soldiers to watch the company. He found France enmeshed in civil war and was unable to procure reinforcements for the small settlement. Meanwhile, the colonists killed their leader in a mutinous uprising and put out to sea in a crudely built boat. They were finally picked up by an English ship and brought back to France.

Two years later Admiral Cologni headed another colonial expedition of Huguenots under the protection of Laudonniere. Avoiding the harbor of Port Royal, site of the ill-fated settlement, they landed on the shore of the St. James River, territory already claimed by Spain, and built a fort. Those who wanted to return to France, many convicts among them, were allowed two ships to do so, but they began to practice piracy instead. The remaining colonists, on the point of starvation, had decided to break up the settlement when Captain Ribault happily returned from France with reinforcements and fresh supplies.

Meanwhile King Philip II of Spain was determined to establish claim to the New World by conquest of Florida and annihilation of the enterprising French Huguenot settlement. He chose Pedro Melendez, a prominent malefactor under sentence to pay a heavy fine, as his emissary to plant a colony of not less than 500 men, of whom 100 should be married men accompanied by their wives. He would be rewarded with 225 square miles of land and an annual income of $2,000.

Within a short time, Pedro Melendez assembled 2,500 people, mostly volunteers from the prisons. A substantial expedition of ships, with sufficient priests on board for spiritual ministrations, left Spain in July 1565 and landed in Florida on September 2. Melendez named the harbor St. Augustine in honor of the Saint's day, and on September 18 a mass was said and the country claimed for Philip II.

The arrival of the Spaniards spelled disaster for the Huguenots. Pedro Melendez decided to sail up the St. James River, but a severe storm destroyed his ships. But he persisted in leading his forces over land, and they killed a great number of the defenseless Huguenot settlers. Only a few escaped the attack and reached the coast, eventually being rescued by passing French ships. Dominie de Gourges, a wealthy Protestant pastor and soldier of Gascony, personally financed and outfitted three ships manned by 50 seamen, and, surprising the Spanish fort, took revenge in the name of the Huguenots.

Sir Humphrey Gilbert set out in 1578 with his half brother, Walter Raleigh, and tried unsuccessfully to found a settlement in New France. In the following year, Sir Francis Drake, exploring the Pacific, went on shore in Marin County, California, and claimed the region for Queen Elizabeth of England. Sir Humphrey Gilbert in 1583 headed five ships with 250 men departing from the port of Plymouth to found the first English colony in America in Newfoundland. Queen Elizabeth had granted him a deed to 600 square miles as a reward for his anticipated success.

One ship returned to Plymouth, but the other four reached Newfoundland. When Sir Humphrey climbed a hill to take possession of the land in the name of the Queen, his sailors were attracted by glints of silver in the hillside. They disrupted the ceremony to scoop up all they could carry back to the ships. Losing all restraint, they mutinied, overmastered Sir Humphrey, seized the ships and turned to piracy. Lusting for gold and silver, they attacked Spanish and Portuguese ships lying in the neighboring harbors. One of their ships was lost in a skirmish but the remaining three steered southward. Off the coast of Massachusetts, another ship sank with a hundred colonists on board. Now only two ships of the original fleet remained. Sir Humphrey took command of *Squirrel*, an unseaworthy little frigate, determined to return to England. A great storm arose in mid-ocean and *Squirrel* sank with all on board. The surviving ship reached Falmouth, England, where it was discovered that the "silver" ore was merely mica.

Spain now made it plain to England that she regarded the south of America as New Spain, hers alone by right of discovery and conquest. The New World was, indeed, a vast country, and the English could colonize the northern part of it. Cabot had laid claim to it, and only the shortsightedness of Henry VII prevented the English from actually taking possession of a land of gold and silver. If gold had been found in the south, why not also in Virginia and all the way north?

A great plea for settlers was launched by Queen Elizabeth. In December 1584, an expedition of seven ships under the command of Sir Richard Grenville reached the shores of Virginia, and 110 colonists began to build a colony at Roanoke. After some explorations along the coast, Sir Richard returned to England, taking a Spanish treasure ship on the way, privateering being a well-accepted occupation.

Trouble with the Indians led to deception and murder on the part of the whites and violent retaliation. Their supplies low, the colonists feared to remain, and persuaded Sir Francis Drake, pausing at Roanoke on his way back to London, to take them home with him. Their abandonment of the settlement proved too hasty, for the following day a shipload of supplies arrived, and two weeks later Sir Richard Grenville himself returned from England with three well-stocked ships. Dismayed to find the settlers gone, he left fifteen men on the island in the event they returned and to secure possession.

Another fleet, which left England in 1586 under Sir Walter Raleigh, arrived in Roanoke in July. A month later, Virginia Dare was born, the first English child of the New World. The fifteen men left a year before had all been killed by the Indians. Nevertheless, the new settlers were determined to remain, and laid the foundation of the future town of Roanoke. Governor White returned to England for reinforcements and came back in the spring of 1590, only to find the site deserted with no trace of the 108 colonists. Roanoke is the lost settlement of American history.

In 1602 Sir Walter Raleigh expended $200,000 of his own fortune to foster another settlement. Captain Bartholomew Gosnold sailed in the *Concord* with a large company and safely reached the coast of Maine. Skirting Cape Cod, he sailed on to Buzzard Bay, where a small colony only endured for four months. Death claimed Queen Elizabeth in April 1603, and her collateral relative James Stuart, King of Scotland, came to the throne as James I. A small expedition of two ships was sent out. The *Speedwell* and the *Discoverer* both reached Maine and continued on to Massachusetts. At Martha's Vineyard they took on a load of sassafras and returned to England.

Meanwhile a group of merchants in Rouen, France, was the first to organize a private company to do business in the New World, commissioning Samuel de Champlain to establish a fur-trading post in the area of the St. Lawrence River. Champlain selected the site of Quebec for a fort, then returned to France. Volunteers were sought by the promise of religious freedom to any Protestant Huguenot willing to emigrate to America. Sovereignty of all the land between Philadelphia and Montreal was even extended to a prominent Huguenot, Monsieur de Monts. In March 1604, two ships bearing colonists reached the Bay of Fundy. Some settled there, the rest went on to Nova Scotia, where they were joined by the first group the following spring. On November 4, 1605, these settlers founded the first permanent French settlement in America, naming the town Port Royal.

Also as a private venture, the Earl of Southampton arranged for an expedition to explore the Atlantic coast and to trade with the Indians. A few Indians brought back to England by Captain George Waymouth aroused much interest there in the New World. Early in 1606, the London Company was organized as a joint-stock enterprise, the subscribers calling themselves adventurers, and only noblemen, gentlemen and merchants were eligible to buy shares. With some misgivings, King James signed the charter on April 10, 1606, granting an enormous area of land to the subscribers: from Virginia north to Passamaquoddy Bay and westward to the Pacific Ocean.

About the same time, the King issued a second patent to the Plymouth Company to establish a colony at their own expense, with English colonists only, under English law and under the Church of England. The London Company was more successful at first in attracting funds and colonists. Experiencing difficulties later, it changed its name to the Virginia Company, but collapsed in 1624, after voting large tracts of land in America to its officers and shareholders. The balance of the vast landholdings reverted to the Crown.

The first ship for the Plymouth Company sailed in August 1606, but was captured by a Spanish man-of-war. A second ship reached the New World and remained until the spring of 1607, its captain and crew returning with glowing reports. Over a hundred colonists arrived at the mouth of the River Kennebec that summer and founded the St. George settlement, constructing a fortification and storehouse as well as dwellings. Only 45 people were willing to remain during the bitter winter, when the storehouse burned down and supplies ran low. Many did not survive, and when summer came the remnant of the colony returned to England.

Why did people leave England to suffer and die in the uncharted areas of the New World? The times were harsh and unfavorable to good living, with change and unrest everywhere brought about by political, economic, and religious forces. It should be remembered that more people migrated to other English possessions than came to the Atlantic seaboard. Between 1620 and 1642, Barbados received 18,600 English emigrants, compared with only 14,000 for Massachusetts during the same period. Likewise, some 18,000 went to other West Indies islands, compared with less than 4,000 to the rest of New England. The Massachusetts settlement of which the Pilgrims were a part was merely an episode in a much broader migratory movement to the New World. The burden of this book is to tell why this small group exerted such a never-to-be-forgotten influence on America's history and development.

The London Company dispatched three ships, the *Discovery*, the *Godspeed* and the *Susan Constant*, on December 9, 1606, under command of Captain Christopher Newport, Captain John Smith and Captain Edward Wingfield. These vessels carried 120 men in all, with no women or children. Among them was George Percy, eighth son of the Earl of Northumberland. Sailing by way of the Canary Islands and the West Indies, they were en route for three and a half months, during which 15 men expired. Finally they entered Chesapeake Bay, calling the entry Point Comfort, sailed up a broad river, which they named the James for their King, and moored the ships about fifty miles upstream. The men eagerly went ashore and found a suitable site for a fortification. In a brief ceremony, Commander Newport opened a sealed box from the London Company containing a set of statutes for the colony and the names of seven men who would form their local government. Captain Wingfield, whose mother was a cousin of Queen Elizabeth, was named President, Robert Hunt became Chaplain. Captain John Smith, then chained in the hold for "fomenting dissension," was made a member of the council.

Founded on the edge of a swamp, Jamestown was the first permanent English settlement in America. Hardship set in, the inevitable companion of new colonies. During the first summer of 1607, half the men died of disease, and the corn they had harvested was devoured by rats. However, defeat was kept at bay by the incredible John Smith, who had become President of the small settlement. Short, sturdy, with beard and mustache, Smith always wore his soldier's uniform, kept a sword at his side, and walked with his chin characteristically thrust forward. His military career began at 16, when he sold his school books and clothes for passage to Holland, where he served the Dutch in their war against Spain. It was his ability to speak Dutch which made the Pilgrims of Leyden favor him in their dealings to secure passage to America.

Tales of Smith's bravery in securing food for the settlement are legion. One famous story told of his capture by the Indians and trial before Chief Powhatan, in which he was condemned to death. He was saved from execution by Pocahontas, the younger daughter of the Chief, who sprang from her seat and clasped the prisoner's head in her arms, pleading for his life. Smith was set free and not until seven years after the death of Pocahontas, who became the wife of colonist John Rolfe, did he relate the story in his *General History*, published in 1624.

Injured in an accident when his powder bag burst into flames, Smith had to return to England to recover from his burns. With his departure the colony lost ground. Food supplies ran low; murder was committed. Smith published a book to defend his administration and rushed to return, but the London Company refused his further services. It was then that he decided to serve the Plymouth Company and assist in settling the northern territory of New England.

The inhabitants of Jamestown suffered many hardships. By the fall of 1607, 76 of the 104 original settlers were dead. In 1616 only 350 of the 1,600 sent by the Company were still alive, and in 1624, despite the fact that there had been more than 4,000 arrivals since the colony's founding, only 1,200 managed to survive Indian attacks and the vicissitudes of life in the wilderness. The verdict of history is that without the aggressive leadership and heroism of Captain John Smith, Jamestown undoubtedly would have suffered a fate similar to that of the Roanoke settlement. It was not until 1616, when an improved method of curing Virginia's tobacco was discovered, that the ultimate success of this colony was assured.

In 1610, King James of England returned to the Dutch their ship, the *Half Moon*, which he had confiscated. That year, in company of several other Dutch ships, the *Half Moon* went to the banks of the Hudson River to trade in furs. Business was brisk, and in 1611 and 1612 a succession of Dutch vessels made profitable trips to the New World. Confidence increased to the point that in 1614 the Staten Generall (States General) of Holland passed an act to establish a settlement on Manhattan Island. That summer a fortification and dwellings were built, and the place named New Amsterdam. Captain Adrian Block explored Long Island, the Connecticut River, and Massachusetts as far as Cape Cod. Another Dutch Captain, Christianson, sailed up the Hudson River to Castle Island near Albany, where he erected a blockhouse and called the nucleus of settlement Fort Nassau.

The Dutch were persistent. Still another Captain, Cornelius Mei (May) sailed past a cape in New Jersey and named it for himself. He proceeded as far as the Bay of Delaware and returned to Holland. All of the land visited was claimed and named New Netherlands. The intention of the Dutch was to profit by trading gin and guns for furs, not to form permanent settlements.

In England the system of primogeniture drove many sons of the gentry to emigrate, just as poor economic conditions sent many peasants to seek their fortune elsewhere. Conditions differed in the Dutch Republic. Estates did not belong solely to the first born son, and important imports such as pepper and curry energized the workingman into financial independence. Trade with the Spice Islands of the East Indies had created a general prosperity, so that few Dutchmen felt inclined to remove to a faraway wilderness. New Netherlands thus developed slowly. It was easy to find a governor for the new possessions, but a butcher, a baker and a candlestick maker were more difficult to come by.

About this time the Protestant party came into political power in France, and in 1612 Monsieur Conde, the protector of Protestants, was installed as Viceroy of the French colony in America. Samuel de Champlain was dispatched for the third time to Quebec. A deeply religious man, he took along a number of Franciscan monks to preach among the Indians, but these friars and the Protestant Huguenots of Quebec quarreled so fiercely that the settlement was almost annihilated.

Meanwhile Captain John Smith had formed a partnership with four wealthy London merchants interested in trading for furs within the limits of the Plymouth grants. On March 3, 1614, he sailed from the Thames with two vessels. He had been commissioned to secure whales, gold and copper or fish and furs. That summer he traded along the coast of Maine. Many schools of whales were seen but the Englishmen had no means to secure them. The 50,000 pounds of fish they caught were barely enough to cover the expenses of the voyage. Captain Smith used the opportunity to explore and map the shore from Penobscot to Cape Cod. In November he returned to Plymouth, England, and persuaded Sir Ferdinand Gorges to colonize. Gorges sailed with two vessels in March 1615, one of 200 tons and one of 50 tons. After three weeks of stormy weather, both ships had to return to England.

In June 1615, Smith set out once more in a vessel of 60 tons under Captain Edmund Chambers. Four French privateers seized his ship, rifled the stores, dispersed the sailors over their own ships, and placed a prize crew aboard. But the French Captain Pyrune, finding the vessel in too poor condition to be of use to him, put Captain Smith and his crew back on board and bade them go. Sculling and bailing, the men managed to reach the harbor of Rochelle in France, where they were taken prisoners. Not until December did Captain Smith succeed in escaping in a rowboat and making his way back to London. In June 1616, he published his New World experiences in a book titled *A Description of New England*, revealing a vast virgin land peopled with free men. Of the colonists he wrote, "I could call them my children for they have been my wife, my hawks, my hounds, my cards and my dice."

Leaving the London Company in 1617, Captain Smith was retained by the Plymouth Company, which was superseded by the Council of Plymouth, upon whose 40 members King James conferred almost unlimited privileges. All were given land in the New World lying between the 40th and 48th parallels of northern latitude and extending from ocean to ocean. Colonization plans from then on were projected in all earnestness, and the King appointed John Smith Admiral of New England for life.

It would not be the destiny of the group of Separatists who left England and lived in Holland until 1620, to come under any of the companies or patents thus far evolved.

James P. Leynse
Claremont, California
May 25, 1971

Chapter 1

SCROOBY, ENGLAND

The arrival of the 17th century was a bold time in England. The 1400s had been more or less stable, the 1500s enterprising, but the 1600s were mad. That distant wilderness called America was to blame, or more particularly, the tobacco which came from there.

It began when Columbus and his crew landed in the West Indies and observed the natives smoking rolls of dried leaves, already an ancient practice among them. They sat around a fire and inhaled smoke from the wonder plant, sucking it through pieces of hollow wood stuck into their nostrils. Tobacco, they said, had a great healing power, and produced satisfaction and contentment when inhaled through a clay pipe. When Columbus brought back some tobacco leaves, they created a stir in Europe.

Despite habit-forming properties due to nicotine and related alkaloids, tobacco was hailed as a new medicine for man's benefit, with powers to ameliorate bronchitis, asthma and rheumatism. It was cultivated by the Spaniards in Haiti before 1535. The natives there first used the word *tobaco* to designate the smoking tube or taking of snuff, but it was adopted by the Spanish as the name of the product itself. When Jacques Cartier explored Canada, he found the Indians drying tobacco leaves in the sun and smoking powdered leaves in pipes made of stone and wood. When Sir Richard Grenville returned to England from Virginia in 1585, he introduced pipe smoking as practiced by the Indians; for a half century it was used medicinally. But

35

in the first half of the 17th century indulgence for pleasure became general. Amsterdam and Rotterdam were leading distribution centers for American-grown tobacco.

Many itinerant traders with a pack of merchandise on their backs became solid store-owning merchants dealing in tobacco, corn and coffee. As barter disappeared, the European world needed more and more gold for its trade coins. The natives of America and the Dutch East Indies were no longer satisfied to receive barrels of salt and rolls of silk in exchange, but England had no gold nor silver and Europe very little. In the mountains of Austria, Saxony, and Spain, small amounts of the valuable yellow mineral were found, but not enough to satisfy the needs of the rapidly growing new trade. Hewers of wood and drawers of water began to ask for coined shillings and pennies instead of grain in exchange.

There was no question that gold was needed, and prayers for it were looked upon with favor by the Anglican Church. The Christian Church had always laid great stress on the importance of finances and the possession of property, whereas Oriental religions, especially Buddhism, were indifferent to business dealings, considering them mundane.

The use of tobacco, both as personal indulgence and commercial commodity, met with initial opposition. The bishops frowned upon the smoking habit, but fines and even imprisonment could not stop it. Smoking by men, even in church, became customary as a sign of modern man's independence from tradition. Life was gay at the outset of the 17th century. Pursuit of pleasure became the most important goal for many who flouted the old and stable ways.

The changes taking place in religion affected daily life. At first Henry VIII had encouraged reform of the Church in his opposition to the Pope, but he bridled when the common people expressed independence of judgment in religious matters and freedom of conscience. This was a new way of thinking. By tradition they had no rights except to believe and do what

they were told. Church officials ordered the people to conform
or be taken into custody, and the more stubborn were brought
to the stake or the gallows as heretics.

In 1539 Henry VIII's Six Articles proclaimed the retention
of the confessional, private masses, and celibacy of the priests.
They further required that all must believe, or profess to believe, in the ritual of wine and wafers quite literally becoming
the blood and body of the Savior, which was the survival of a
primitive religious blood rite. Ideas would change when Henry
broke with Rome in order to divorce Catherine of Aragon and
marry Anne Boleyn. For one thing, he forbade the worship of
idols, and the royal treasury conveniently possessed itself of the
gold, silver and precious jewels of the churches. By royal de-
cree every church had to have a Bible for public reading of the
scriptures in English, not in Latin. This was a revolutionary innovation, indeed, as for the first time people in England who
could read only the vernacular were able to examine the Holy
Writ and come to their own conclusions without the help of the
clergy. In this was contained the origin of the idea of freedom
of conscience or independent judgment which the Separatists
were vehemently to demand for themselves.

King Henry's bishops tried to prevent the reading of the
Bible at Mass as well as open discussion of the passages read.
Then, as if he had not broken the bond with Rome, the King
commanded his subjects to continue to observe "the holy bread
and wafer, creeping to the cross, setting up lights before arti-
facts of Jesus Christ, bearing of candles and the rest." Many
erudite and distinguished men were executed or thrown into
filthy dungeons for refusing religious conformity to the royal
will. Among those who lost their heads was Sir Thomas More,
the most prominent literary figure in the reign of Henry VIII.
His famous book *Utopia*, like Plato's *Republic* and Sir Philip
Sidney's *Arcadia*, pictures an imaginary kingdom on an island
in the New World where the laws, customs and life of the people
are ideal. This was an eloquent protest against the brutality of

the times, the religious intolerance and many social ills. *Utopia* foresaw a literate people living in clean cities where the dignity of the individual was respected, and men were allowed to choose their own religion.

Henry took radical action. He dissolved the monasteries, confiscating huge church estates in the name of the crown and using their wealth to reward loyalty and services to him of the nobility. The Pope therefore regarded England as a country in rebellion, an outlaw in the family of Catholic nations, and decreed that Englishmen owed no allegiance to Henry, an illegitimate monarch. Henry's Articles were repealed when his only son, Edward VI, a boy of nine, came to the throne with the powerful Duke of Somerset as his protector. Now the country began to turn Protestant. In the reign of Edward (1547-1553), the first copy of the *English Book of Common Prayer* appeared, prepared by Archbishop Thomas Cranmer. The first step in establishing a Protestant church service was taken in 1552 with the publication of the *Edwardian Service Book.*

The course of Protestantism, however, was slowed by the death of young Edward, who was succeeded by his sickly half sister Mary, daughter of Henry VIII and Catherine of Aragon. Mary, a fanatical Catholic, immediately recognized the Pope as spiritual and temporal overlord of Europe including England. She re-established Roman Catholic rites in the churches. Ruthless and bigoted, Bloody Mary brooked no heresy in her realm; she had hundreds of Protestants killed in Kent alone. To save their lives, many Protestant leaders fled from the country, taking refuge in Geneva, Basle, Frankfort and Strasbourg. The horror of her four-year reign ended with her death in 1551, when Elizabeth, daughter of Henry VIII and Anne Boleyn, came to the throne. Elizabeth broke with Rome and was roundly denounced by the Pope as a bastard with no legal claim to the throne. The Pope had every Catholic court in Europe support the claims of Mary, Queen of Scots and France, as the legal successor. While she supported the Anglican Church, Elizabeth disliked radical reformers.

The Tudor monarchs, Henry VIII and his daughter Elizabeth, were tyrants, even dictators, but they knew how to win over the people with pomp and splendor and fleshpots. The Tudors were clever. They could accomplish more by a fine dinner and bottles of good wine than by decrees and laws. True, the common man tasted little of those splendid dinners, but he could feast his eyes on the grandeur of the Tudors and admire their glittering royal trappings.

When Queen Elizabeth died in 1603 after a long reign of 45 years, her Stuart cousin James I became King. The Stuarts were Scottish Presbyterians. As Scottish rulers they did not know compromise, and as Presbyterians had little sense of festivity and humor. Careless King James did not seem to fit the 1600s, when people flouted tradition in an age of intellectual expansion and geographical discoveries. Two months before his birth, his mother Mary Stuart, Queen of Scots, watched in horror as her husband, Lord Darnley, murdered David Rizzio, her confidential secretary who was rumored to be her lover and father of the unborn child. The world had been cruel to his mother, and the world was cruel to James VI of Scotland, who became James I of England. He was not attractive in his person or demeanor, but the English had learned to accept with forbearing coarse, ignorant and superstitious rulers on the throne. In James, they had also a besotted, rapacious one who walked uncertainly on spindly legs, his head too large for his body and his ill appearance only emphasized by his glittering array of jewels and richly embroidered garments. Even more than his Scottish burr when he spoke, the people disliked his perverted sense of humor and his disregard for human beings. It was, indeed, a bitter pill to swallow when a Scot signed the death warrant of an Englishman with a crude remark such as "This rat is better out of this world than in it."

Even more than his personal inadequacies, the people disliked him for being pro-Spain. To James I, the King of Spain was the greatest monarch on earth. In spite of his training in Presbyterian theology, James I was a Roman Catholic at heart. That his Protestant subjects hated the very name of Catholic Philip meant little to James as he continued his efforts to find favor with Spain. The English had a good reason for being averse to this country. Many families had lost a son burned as a heretic at the stake by the Spanish Inquisition to bring England back to the true faith. And now it was difficult to determine if their sovereign was Catholic or Protestant. Non-conformity was considered rebellion, so that many well-established Englishmen became poverty-stricken refugees in free Holland.

It was an era in which material success was openly pursued. The homes of the prosperous were symbols of worldly progress. Oaken furniture gave way to carved walnut, coated with gold leaf. Wall tapestries were replaced by rich coverings of silk, sometimes in striking black and gold stripes. Ceilings were painted in gold as background for voluptuous nude female figures, and bedrooms were hung with rich gold cloth. The color of gold was in high fashion as a sign of the times, highlighted by floors of black and white Genoese marble. The wealthy favored a gaudy abundance of gilt everywhere in their living quarters.

Costumes were equally elegant, with slashed sleeves preferred by young women to disclose the silken fabric of their undergarments. They enveloped themselves in a scent of musk, copying the ways of French ladies. They wore a farthingale or hoop to support the back of their dresses, and placed the wire understructure of their farthingales on the floor in a corner of the room before sitting down. Wide ruffs attached to a wire frame around the neck were in fashion, and hair was swept up with artificial wiglets added. Bodices were cut so low in decolleté that the resulting cleavage reached to the abdomen. Small black beauty patches adorned well-painted faces, and eyes looked out boldly at men through black velvet vizards. Ladies

wore high-heeled shoes or heelless Turkish sandals which revealed painted toenails.

Men of fashion were equally colorful in their attire. A
gentleman wore as many as eight rings to match the color
scheme of his clothes, and polished his fingernails pink. Lace
jabots decorated his beautifully sewn shirt and a jaunty feather
was in his cap. A green plume held by a diamond button was the
acme of elegance. Those beribboned fops! The beau used scent
bottles which he carried with him, and touched up his curls with
an ivory comb. Silken hose covered handsome calves above red-
heeled shoes. Doublets were brocaded with roses; rosettes decorated silvered shoes.

Deer-baiting, cock fights, and horse races were favorite
amusements. Both sexes enjoyed the fairs with their lively pup-
pet shows, rope dancers, and culinary offerings of roast pigs and
gingerbread, but most surprising of all to the elders was that
young men, even of the middle class, wanted their own horses
for riding, disdaining the lowly mule. A horse owner happily
had the hooves of his horse painted with gold and his own feet
shod with silver.

Older men scented and curled their beards and chewed on
cloves to scent the breath. A silver fork was carried in a case
for eating at taverns. One no longer had to sop up gravy with
slabs of bread. Instead a small piece of bread at the end of the
fork was dipped in the gravy. A wealthy nobleman maintained
a footman, a page, a blackamoor and serving women. Imitation
was the thing. The petty noblesse copied the nobility; the shop-
keeper copied the merchant, and the laborer tried to keep up
with his employer. Candles impregnated with spices and flowers
perfumed the rooms as scullery women whisked drops of pep-
permint water about the floors and into the corners where the
dogs slept.

Condemnation was preached from many a Calvinistic pulpit. The Puritans organized to remedy the extreme materialism
of their times. They did not want to separate themselves from

the Church of England but to purify the ritual and to correct the worldly power of the bishops and their soldiers over the populace. They wanted to live strictly according to the precepts of the Bible. The Lollards had instituted similar reforms in the 14th century. They were followers of John Wycliffe of Yorkshire, who attacked many of the practices of the Roman Church. The Lollards, derisively called so from a medieval word for mumblers because they prayed constantly, were gradually driven into the background, but their precepts were taken up by the Bohemian John Huss and eventually absorbed in the larger wave of Martin Luther's Reformation. Wycliffe as pastor had consecrated a number of lay preachers to proclaim the separation of "saints and sinners."

Eventually the Lollards were eliminated as a sect by intense persecution. The Puritans, however, proved a more persistent sort. They were opposed to any system which supported a priesthood and set forms of dogma. They aimed at abolishing the clergy who stood between the individual and God, and to restore intimate, personal contact with the Deity. They also disapproved of the Anglican Church's concern with property and costly vestments. One could call them forerunners of the Presbyterians, since they originated the idea of government by elders.

William Laud, Bishop of London, later Archbishop of Canterbury and minister to King Charles I, hated the Puritans. It was through Laud that the bishops were given worldly power and supplied with soldiers and a police court to enforce conformity. His methods were simple. He listed all clergymen in the realm and placed an "O" after the name of those who were orthodox, meaning those who obeyed his orders, and a "P" after the names of Puritans. He had the tongues of all the P's clipped, a move which drove their leader, Thomas Cartwright, out of England to seek refuge in Holland with a large number of his congregation.

The name Puritan was by 1564 applied frequently to those

in England who sought to modify or to purify the worship of the State Church. On the other hand, the Separatists were the more zealous reformers within the Puritan movement. At first they were not known as such, in fact had no name, not feeling the need, but simply calling themselves "We" or "Us," and sometimes "Saints" and "Separatists." Actually the term Pilgrim did not come into common use until 1840.

It must be remembered that the Elizabethans were fond of controversy. They were sharp witted, given to engaging in lively arguments, expressing themselves in the zestful language of Christopher Marlowe, the dramatist who invented blank verse, and in the poetry of William Shakespeare. Rhetoric frequently dispensed with polite circumlocutions. Catholicism was called "the whore of Rome." An Elizabethan enjoyed the pleasures of the table, bottle and bed. He married early and often, sometimes within a few weeks of losing a mate, and had numerous children. Blacks and grays were the usual costumes worn for the Sabbath, otherwise the Elizabethans wore russet browns and Lincoln greens, the colors of England's lower classes. Some had large and varied wardrobes, such as that of William Brewster of the Scrooby group who had "a red cap, a white cap, a quilted cap, a lace cap, a vilet coat and one pair of green drawers."

It was an age of confusion and contention in which two irreconcilable philosophies of life were engaged in mortal dispute, beginning with Martin Luther's action in 1517 when he nailed his 95 theses to the door of Wittenberg Cathedral, in a daring challenge to the autocratic pretensions of the Holy See of Rome and its patent abuses. Luther attacked the Pope, and thus shook all of Christendom to its foundations, releasing great latent forces. These crept alarmingly over the continent and extended to England in a democratic revolution known as the Reformation. It brought in its wake great social, economic and political changes, which were ruthlessly resisted by the monarchs and ruling classes.

The wave of opposition to change took the form of persecution of the non-conformists in England, such as the Puritans and the Separatists. The Pilgrim group, whose adventures we will follow from the organization of their first congregation in Scrooby, England, to their migration to the New World, played a major role in the conflict of spiritual and material forces which shaped our modern world. In a brave struggle to realize a nobler conception of living which would recognize the innate dignity and worth of each individual person, they achieved the separation of church and state.

The Separatists established an independent Congregational church at Scrooby and nearby Gainsborough. Scrooby is the narrow northern tip of Nottinghamshire, squeezed between Lincolnshire on one side and Yorkshire on the other. The hamlet of Scrooby lies just off the Great North Road about half way between London and the Scottish border, approximately in the center of England. It is on the banks of the River Ryton where it drains the moors and fen lands of the middle eastern counties. The countryside is rather poor and sparsely settled. Its cottages and small houses, occupied now by tenant farmers and field hands, have changed little since the time of the Separatists. Their descendants are still seen plowing and planting the land, weeding and hoeing and harvesting crops. However, it is less isolated now than when it was a mean townlet four hundred years ago, with its small parish church beside the Ryton, though it is still a property of the Archbishopric of York, just as it has been for almost one thousand years.

The imposing Manor House of the 15th and 16th centuries in Scrooby was surrounded by a moat in the manner of a castle. It had forty rooms and its own private chapel. The main facade was partly of brick, which faced onto the larger of the two courtyards, partly of half-timber construction. A flight of stone steps led to a great oaken door which opened into the vast baronial hall where the archbishop and lords of the realm held court on their rare visits ordained by the papal see. It was still an imposing structure when the Brewster family moved in and occupied a part of it. At that time some small houses remained nearby and two or three large stables, kennels, dovecotes, a granary, blacksmith's shop, bake house and brew house. There was also a tavern maintained for the royal courtiers and travelers along the Great North Road between London and the North Country.

The Archbishop of York used the Manor House to confer with Anglican ministers of the North Country over problems of State and Church, like the suppressions of revolts and punishment of rebels and heretics. But on occasion there was gaiety, as the Archbishop frequently invited the ministers to eat and drink and hunt abundant game in the forests, moors and swamps.

Then, too, the Bishop of the area and his ministers came to the Manor House to see bear-baiting and games and dancing after church services, and to participate in the Maypole sports. This levity on the Sabbath greatly irked the Puritans and the Separatists, who called the sport of the Maypole "ye stinking idol" of the Anglican Church. The Manor House, with its tavern and brew-house and its visitors and travelers, was a place of hospitality. Many an evening the rafters rang with song and laughter, and applause given touring actors.

The great hall used for assemblies and balls was furnished with three screens, six large oaken tables and nine long benches, a huge carved cupboard and a broad carved desk. In a separate chapel were chairs, a wooden altar, and two smaller stone altars which could be placed over the former for special occasions. The rich tones of two organs reverberated through the entire Manor House.

Since it was situated on the highway, the Manor House was often the scene of colorful and historic occasions. The ceiling of the banquet room had carved oak beams above richly panelled walls. On his way to the Court in London, the Archbishop of Canterbury, who traveled with a magnificent retinue when he visited the Queen, would be accompanied by a hundred attendants in livery of scarlet silk. The Archbishop would dine in 16th-century splendor with his company, as fine wines flowed and delicious aromas rose from the kitchens and dining room.

In 1503 Margaret Tudor, elder daughter of Henry VII, stayed overnight at the Manor House on her way north to marry James IV of Scotland. This marriage eventually brought the Stuarts to the English throne. Cardinal Wolsey came to the Manor House in the summer of 1530 when he was banished from the favor of King Henry VIII. Thomas Cromwell then moved in to shape the monarch's government and institute the English Reign of Terror. Cardinal Wolsey had urged diplomacy with the Pope; Cromwell advised Henry to cease negotiating for a divorce from Catherine of Aragon, but instead renounce the jurisdiction of Rome, declare himself supreme head of the Church of England and then obtain a divorce from his own courts. His policy swept Cardinal Wolsey to disgrace and death before the year was finished.

Queen Elizabeth and James I, passing by the old Manor House, found it somewhat decayed and in disrepair. Both tried to secure it for use as a hunting lodge. The Elizabethans enjoyed hunting and sports, but never swam or even bathed, having a distaste for water. The manor is now completely gone, and all that remains for the visitor to see is the small church of St. Wilfred's and some remnants of the manorial walls. The crumbling mansion was finally demolished in 1637 and a farm house erected in its stead, but a plaque commemorates it as the residence once of a commoner, William Brewster, from 1575-1608, "where he organized the Pilgrim Church of which he became the ruling elder and with which he removed in 1608 to Amsterdam and in 1609 to Leyden and in 1620 to Plymouth, Massachusetts where he died April 16, 1644." He died in 1643, not 1644. The mistake was first made three centuries ago by Nat Morton in copying from William Bradford's *History* into the Plymouth Church records.

The Brewsters were an ancient British family of the upper middle class, listed in the gentry of Norfolk as far back as 1375. Born in 1565, a year after Elizabeth of the Tudors came to the throne, William Brewster was ten years old when his parents went to live at the Manor House in Scrooby. His mother's name was Prudence. His father, William Brewster, was made a bailiff and overseer and collector of rents, fees and fines by Archbishop Grindal in 1575. For these services he received the use of the Manor House and the fruits of its grounds and in addition $165.00 a year. His father also had to provide food and drink and a change of horses for the couriers of the Queen who came riding in and out at all hours of the day and night. Before the days of the stagecoach—there were only a dozen of them in the whole kingdom and most of them in London— the Great North Road was little more than a trail, ungraded, unfenced, along which a horse and coach could travel only five miles an hour in the winter. The elder William Brewster made certain improvements in the Manor House. For instance, he replaced the straw sacks and wooden pillows with feather beds, and put in the first chimney of the neighborhood.

The Manor House remained William Brewster's home for 33 years. He left it only to attend school or for employment. In the year 1580, when he was 15, he entered Cambridge University in the ancient, walled town with its 14 colleges. The entire curriculum had a religious cast, since its prime purpose was to provide clergymen for the realm. From the beginning, William identified himself with a Reform Circle and a Colony of Puritans. Some students disagreed with the regimentation by the Crown, the authority of the Church, each other's religion, and each other's way of life. In his choice of association, William was influenced by two of his classmates, John Greenwood, a theological student, and Robert Devereux, Second Earl of Essex.

John Greenwood, who was born to wealth and reared at court became a martyr to his beliefs. He was a bold nonconformist and a fearless Puritan, a dangerous stance at the time. Upon graduation he became Chaplain to Lord Rich, but soon accepted the leadership of the Puritans in London. There he was thrown into a filthy jail together with his young friend Henry Barrow, another Puritan. The men were confined for years, until on March 24, 1593, they were suddenly removed to Tyburn for execution on religious grounds. However, William Brewster went in great haste to the Earl of Essex and Lord Burghley, and by his eloquence persuaded them to halt the execution. The Archbishop strenuously objected. Had he not hanged men and women members of the Puritan and Separatist movement before for the crime of choosing their own pastors? Now the Bishop's private police had two Puritan pastors in custody, and in the name of the State Church he demanded their immediate execution. There was no help for it, and within a week, the two men were brought to the gallows and summarily hanged.

Young Robert Devereux, Earl of Essex, became friends with William Brewster at Cambridge, and both secretly attended meetings of the Separatists. Devereux disapproved of bishops having military power. However, his high social position and close connection with the Crown forbade him to join the Separatist movement openly, it would have been dangerous not only to himself but to his family.

William Brewster had been at Cambridge for two years when he was asked by the Earl of Essex to enter the service of Ambassador Sir William Davison as his private secretary. When he left the University in 1583, his mode of living changed. He attended Court functions, dressed impressively in a coat of violet silk, with a fluted ruff around his neck, yellow velvet breeches and blue silk stockings. To his gratification, he found Sir William a man of deeply religious convictions, who was in favor of the Separatist movement. Brewster accompanied the Ambassador to Scotland and returned with him to London and the Court in 1584. Two months thereafter, the Ambassador took him on a confidential mission to Holland.

William Brewster liked the Netherlands immediately, and it was always to hold a special place in his affections. He served Sir William Davison so enthusiastically, with pen and heart, that the official introduced the young man to many distinguished people. Brewster spent his first night in Holland in Middelburg, the capital of the south, where the English Ambassador concluded a treaty in the name of Queen Elizabeth with the Dutch against the invasion and tyranny of Spain, making the Netherlands a protectorate of England. When the Ambassador proceeded to The Hague, the capital of the Netherlands, Brewster remained behind in Middelburg to welcome the Earl of Essex and the Earl's step-father, the Earl of Leicester. On the morning of October 10, 1585, cannon shots announced the arrival of the English delegation. The Earl of Essex, as personal representative of the Queen, was even then a young man with great power and widely-sought influence.

An imposing fleet of ships bore the group of English lords, knights, captains and soldiers to implement the treaty between the Netherlands and England. The Earl of Leicester was made General-in-Chief of the Dutch Army. The widow of Prince Willem of Orange, with her son Maurice, the heir apparent, had taken up their residence in Middelburg for the purpose of entertaining their guests with seven days of feasting. During these festivities, Brewster stayed with the Earl of Essex and his step-father, and was asked to accompany these nobles in the triumphal procession to The Hague.

It was the Christmas season of 1585, and in every castle and town house along the road there were music and feasting, with meat and wine in abundance. Candles sparkled in great brass chandeliers. At Rotterdam, the great harbor city, the buildings were illuminated at night brighter than had ever been witnessed before. At Delft, the party stayed at the palace of

Orange, where only a year before the Spanish had assassinated Prince Willem, the beloved father of his country.

The entrance of the delegation into The Hague was a glorious spectacle. By this time the procession had increased to 300 horsemen of the British nobility on prancing steeds in magnificent pageantry. The vanguard included Dutch pikemen, musketeers and citizenry, who always followed a military display. At The Hague, quarters were allotted to the cooks, stable men, musicians, gypsies and entertainers gathered to provide gaiety and largesse for the English nobility.

William Brewster stayed with the Earls at the Palace of the House of Orange, where a reception for the Ambassador and his party was followed by feasts, torchlight parades, fireworks, and an endless array of parties. At one evening function, the Regent of Holland honored the Earl of Essex by placing around his neck a heavy gold chain of rare Dutch workmanship. When they had returned to their rooms at the Palace of the House of Orange, the young Earl put the chain around Brewster's neck, in token of their warm-hearted friendship. "Wear it," he told him. "Wear it until we are back in England; then I shall have to present it to the Queen."

The English entourage of 300 horsemen entered the city of Leyden on January 3, 1586, making a magnificent showing. They were received at the city gate by Johan Lord Ripperts-van Groenendyck, one of the well known burgomasters of Leyden, who escorted them to the Town Hall along streets brightened by masses of flowers decorating the lamp posts and lined with cheering people. Costly tapestries and flags fluttered from many a balcony crowded with spectators. The party entered the Town Hall under a great canopy of vivid colors.

During their days in Holland, the friendship between William Brewster and Robert Devereux deepened. The Earl of Essex took part in many religious meetings with his Scrooby friend, and was almost persuaded to make an open break with the Anglican Church. But this would have meant giving up his life at the London Court. He wrote to Queen Elizabeth about his feelings, and went so far as to tell her that bishops should not be magistrates nor have civil authority. The Queen replied in a stern letter, ordering him not to join the Separatist movement. "All men must by law belong to the Anglican Church." she told him. "All men should attend its services and be under the authority of the bishops and pastors."

To this the Earl replied: "The only officers of a true Church should be those named in the Bible: pastors, teachers, elders, deacons and widows or deaconesses. The Bible nowhere states that the Church should be controlled by the state and have bishop-magistrates."

When the Queen's letter came it said warningly: "Do not hold or meddle with those malcontents, those Separatists or Saints." As for William Brewster, in spite of his Court service he was in favor of free worship according to the Bible and the rule of his heart. Persecution of the Separatists had sharpened when Brewster returned from Holland. Tales of suffering were brought to the meetings in Scrooby. Executions for infractions of the law were a form of public entertainment, held in an open square. The penalty of beheading was meted out for such minor offenses as the theft from a lord of a gold neck-chain or a pair of boots, or even a bottle of wine.

Were not the Separatists law-breakers? Didn't they disdain the God-given authority of all British people, the Anglican ministry? Why should the Separatists want to read the Bible, the book reserved for the clergy, and ignore the *Book of Common Prayer*, the one written especially for the people! The authorities also objected to the Separatist pastors wearing black suits and black gloves when they preached.

Puritans and the more zealous group of Separatists wore the somber colors to indicate their protest against the worldliness of the times. The soldiery of the bishops would often mock and threaten them for being different, and expose them to the ridicule of passersby. Separatists would reach their hidden meeting place limp with fright. Women members fled at the sight of a group of halberdiers, and some returned stealthily to their homes, afraid to proceed to the meeting of the evening. It was often dangerous even to return home and they had to hide in an alley. Still they would make the effort to attend the next Separatist meeting.

As in all times, those who dared to be different were singled out for persecution which was especially distressing to the children. It was humiliating for a boy to be grabbed by a group of rowdies and placed on top of a beer barrel. "Stand there! Don't you dare to move!" the boys would threaten. "Now, preach to us. Haven't you heard sermons enough by those crows of elders? You dirty dog of a Separatist! Don't you want to preach to us? Here, take this . . . and this . . . and this . . . !" And they would beat him unmercifully with a rope.

The little girls' solemn dresses and white aprons could be spotted from a distance. Often they were targets for wandering street urchins, both girls and boys, who would taunt and threaten, tearing their clothes, ripping the bonnets from their heads and shaking them. "Can't you talk? Haven't you learned how to defend yourselves? Don't your fathers argue all the time?"

In his *History*, William Bradford tells about the presecution in his unadorned seventeenth-century English: "Satan continued to raise his anger against the Saints. Sometimes by bloody death and cruel torture . . . Sometimes by imprisonment and banishment . . . The old serpent prevailed by persecution, torture and tragedy. Against Satan's barbarous force our side labored to have the right to worship . . . There are many new members whose heart the Lord has touched with heavenly zeal. Those, too, are being hunted and persecuted on every side . . . Some are taken in their bed at night and clapt in prison, others have their houses beset and are watched night and day."

Meanwhile political events of great importance led to a drastic state of affairs. Queen Elizabeth wanted to add Mary

Stuart's Scotland to the British possessions. The method would be simple. She told her Foreign Ambassador, Davison, to accuse Queen Mary of Scotland of scheming to have the Spanish fleet override the English one, and to establish the Catholic Church in England. She revealed to him in secret that she intended to demand the head of Queen Mary and explained: "The axe to fall straight, ye exact between chin and collar-bone." Mary was peremptorily arrested and confined to the Tower of London, then beheaded. It was direct enough, but Elizabeth had not counted on the uproar which followed this alarming act of regicide.

Perhaps Elizabeth had reasons to be provoked. Could it be true that Mary had bribed a house-servant of Elizabeth to kill her? Perhaps Elizabeth had in her possession confiscated letters of Mary's disclosing arrangements for the Spanish to annihilate the English fleet and then bring the country into the Catholic Church. Queen Mary and her successor King James unquestionably had Catholic sympathies. But whatever the reasons, Mary's execution was a cruel deed. "It is a horrible accident!" Elizabeth cried, frightened by the threatening consequences. "I had no deal with it!" To quench the furious indignation of the English and Scottish people, Queen Elizabeth found a suitable scapegoat. She accused her Foreign Ambassador of duplicity, disgraced him publicly and fined him Ł10,000, then imprisoned him in the Tower of London, and finally, to settle the guilt on him permanently, she ordered Davison beheaded.

William Brewster was bewildered by these dreadful events. Politics proved to be too strong for him, and he left the service of the Court. How could he abide an intrigue which put to death his patron and dear friend, whom he esteemed so highly? Leaving London, he returned directly to the hamlet of Scrooby, where his family awaited him in the Manor. On April 1, 1598, he was given the office of Postmaster at the Manor at "twenty pence per diem" which was later increased to "two shillings sterling." He was 33 years old and had been living at Scrooby, except for absences for education and employment, for twenty-three years. The next year he married. Much of his time was now devoted to espousing the cause of the Separatist movement.

It was a youthful group. Their pastor, John Robinson, was 30. Deacon Samuel Fuller 23, William Bradford 18. Only a few had reached the age of 40. Brewster, their leader, was a quiet, unostentatious man of humility. He had never studied for the ministry nor was he ordained. He was happy to pass the time with his Bible and a few choice friends. There was in his character a rare mixture of iron and velvet. It never occurred to him to shake the world to pieces and then put it together again, yet he did just that. If one could name a few people as the founders of America, William Brewster would surely be one of them.

Scrooby has been a town since 100 A.D., a town with an inheritance reflected in the facial features of its men and women, who are not typically British. The first to come here were the dark-eyed, black-haired Normans, with their quick temper. Knowing well how to use their long spears and short swords, they did not confine themselves to Scrooby but swarmed all over the North Country, the town of York particularly attracting them. There the Roman Emperor Hadrian had built a house and a wall, whose ruins may still be seen, and there the Emperor Severus died. The Romans gradually withdrew, but some remained behind and left their traces. The Celtic conquerors came and some stayed to leave their blond features stamped on the faces of many a descendant. The Celts were succeeded by the Danes, whom the English roundly hated, but they gave the town its Danish name of Scrooby, meaning village.

The crude Danes, who bred revolt wherever they went, defiled the churches when they carved the forked-lightning zigzags of their Fire God, Thor, right over the church entrance in Scrooby, and the beaks of the raven, their good luck bird, over the doors of other churches in the neighborhood. They finally provoked a wild rebellion against themselves by the quiet, calm and long-suffering serfs of Scrooby. An enraged mob skinned the offenders alive, nailing their skins to the church door, to teach them not to defy the church. The inhumanity of man to man committed in the name of religion has been more heinous than any other.

Other strangers came. William of Normandy sent a vanguard to Scrooby, some of whom remained to live there. During the reign of Elizabeth, 10,000 Dutch refugees from Spanish persecution were allowed to settle around Scrooby, most of them settling in the area of Norwich. Many were Mennonites, wool-workers who came to live peacefully and to teach, for British law required each household to take in an English apprentice. Thus many Englishmen learned the skill of wool-working. Menno Simmons (1492-1559) was the founder of the Mennonite sect in the Netherlands, an Anabaptist movement opposed to infant baptism, taking oaths and military service. This Protestant denomination still flourishes in Europe and the United States. The Mennonites who lived in Scrooby were able to spread their objections to the civic power of the English Church, its bishops and the bishops' soldiery, and so greatly influenced the three parties in opposition to the Crown: the Ancient Brethren, who established their church in Amsterdam, the Puritans and the Separatists.

When William Brewster, like his father before him, became Postmaster of Scrooby, it was still only a market place in a village of 150 persons. Some 60 persons attended Brewster's meetings at the Manor House. Their desire was to express in solidarity their opposition to King James' leanings toward Spain, to the State Church's formalization and enforcement by armed soldiers, and especially to the practice of trial and execution by jurists and hangmen authorized by the Church as well as the Crown.

The Separatist meetings grew in numbers. Soon there were

300 members of the congregation, as people came from nearby Austerfield and Bawty. When the need was felt for more professional spiritual leadership, the Rev. Richard Clyfton was made Pastor and the Rev. John Robinson, Assistant Pastor, William Brewster being elected as Ruling Elder.

The Separatists were in agreement with the Ancient Brethren, a group who had settled in Amsterdam, and the Puritans, who wished to rectify the glaring faults of the Anglican Church, to purity and reform its errors. The Separatists, however, wanted to go a step further and restore direct communication with God without intervention of priests, thus reviving a practice of early Christianity. "Prophesying" they called it, and "testifying" to God's omnipresence and His goodness as the Father of all mankind. The Separatists of Scrooby disapproved of the worldly enjoyments of the time, which were carried to great excess. They frowned upon Sunday dinners, schools for girls, and attending Shakespeare's plays. They even had misgivings about the clock which young Pastor Robinson had on his table. It was a worldly device, as was, too, the sealing of a marriage with a bridal ring, "ye diabolical circle for ye devil to dance in."

Such topics of interest were generally discussed in the entrance hall before the service began. The men stood comfortably around the pipe rack, where a man could claim his own long clay pipe with his personal mark on it and enjoy a smoke while talking about the novelty of young men wearing black skullcaps in church instead of the accepted hats. Why, pray, should men stand up for prayers, yet remain seated during the customary reading of the two or three chapters of the Bible? During the lengthy service, men smoked their pipes and women passed their little scent-boxes and peppermints, customs generally favored. Should a church member wear black gloves for testifying, just as the preacher did for preaching?

Long sermons were expected and endured. When a member fell asleep and the sexton awakened him by tickling his ear with his feather-on-a-pole, the member was reprimanded, but nobody criticized the preacher whose sermon lasted beyond the usual two hours.

Often the deaconess was praised. She was traditionally an ancient and suitable widow who with "ye little birchen rod went about during ye service to beat ye devil out of ye impious little maidens and wretched little boys." Also praised in meeting was the bravery of a new bridegroom and bride of the congregation who had refused to be married by an Anglican priest but were joined in holy wedlock by a civil ceremony. Such couples were severely reprimanded and publicly punished by order of the Bishop. The groom had one or both of his ears cut off and the bride was whipped in the public square to put fear into the hearts of any who contemplated such divergence from the Church. Yet the Separatist couple had remained true to their faith, even though the young husband was ordered by the Bishop to wear for two years a large "S" sewed to his sleeve for "sower of sedition" and the wife had to wear for one year a scarlet "B" on her sleeve for "blasphemer."

As the Anglican Church forbade people to read the Bible, the Separatists, many just learning how to read, had to conceal it in the dough-trough, the wood-box or the family water well behind those two loose bricks.

In the meeting house the men occupied the seats on the right, the women those to the left. The bare room had no altar, no stained glass windows, no organ, as music was thought to be inspired by the devil. Elder Brewster sat on one side of an oaken table and John Robinson at the other while Reverend Clyfton preached with dignity. After Sunday's meeting a cold meat meal was served, prepared the previous day since cooking on the Sabbath was forbidden. The frugal repast comprised cold oatmeal, mutton or pork and beans, or possibly a stew. Meals were simple, cooked in a single black iron pot, which hung on a tripod in the open fireplace. Meat cooked in a thick soup like a stew, into which one could dip pieces of bread, plus a dish of cooked dried apples, was a satisfying dinner. For festive occasions there would be such delicacies as fowl, smoked ham, fish and smoked eel. There was plenty of ale, the drink of any good living Christian. As in Holland, beer was taken for breakfast, at the noon day and evening meal by the whole family. Water, too often contaminated, was avoided.

The family ate around the bare oaken table, in silence for the most part, but with a sense of contentment and understanding companionship. After the meal, the man of the household asked for the book—everyone knew he meant the Bible—and a chapter was read, the family thanked the Lord for the meal, and the children thanked their parents before leaving the table.

Meals and church meetings were the highlights of social life in the isolated hamlet of Scrooby, punctuated by the events of birth, marriage and death. Sunday was meeting day. Families attended together, even taking the babes in arms. The morning service lasted from eight to noon. After refreshment at home, the family returned for the afternoon session, a repetition of the morning ceremonies with different texts used, lasting from two to six in the evening. The meeting opened with a prayer, followed by a reading of one or two chapters of the Bible. The first speaker uttered a prayer, then preached for one to two hours. The second speaker rose to explain the biblical text for another hour or so. On special occasions, even a third and fourth speaker might go to the oaken table, face the congregation, and discourse. Time was always available; it was a rest from work and chores, and often eight long hours were spent in the meeting room.

During the lengthy meeting the children sat on the hard benches and listened, day dreamed, or even dozed off, and then grimly listened some more. Off and on the sexton awoke them with his feather-on-a-pole. Then they listened obediently some more until the droning voice of the preacher in his black clothes, black skull cap and black gloves lulled them to sleep again. If they so much as grimaced at each other to break the monotony, they were sharply rebuked. If they talked to each other, they were corrected by a slap. The only variation in the procedure of the meeting was the hour devoted to prophesying, which meant an opportunity for a very lively discussion in which only the men of the congregation participated.

Though their meetings were deemed unlawful gatherings and the meeting place frequently had to be changed, the faith of the Separatists spread. Similar congregations were formed in the most unexpected places in spite of the fact that many were punished severely when caught, branded on their foreheads with a "B" for "Bible worshipper," or cruelly deformed by having their noses slashed. Often meetings were disbanded in great confusion with the warning cry: "The soldiers! The soldiers are coming!" Armed with lances, swords and clubs, they drove the people out of the meeting house. If by chance the meeting was held in a room of the old Manor House and the Bishop's soldiers arrived, some of the men would run into the tavern room, grab beer jugs and pretend to be there on a drinking bout. That always baffled the soldiers. Many seized in the meeting room were roped together and taken to filthy gaols, where they had to sleep on straw, endure bad food and other conditions injurious to their health and lives, without any decent provision for sanitation.

The harshness of the times was conducive to belief in superstition and witchcraft, so that the Separatists spoke of the devil as if he were a person. To them the evil one actually existed on earth. Men claimed to have seen his shadow, although no man ever had set eyes on him except, as the Bible said, Jesus Christ, the Master. At their meetings, men professed that their women had seen the track of his cloven feet on the garden path and heard him laugh mockingly and threaten, "I'll get you! I'll put my hands on you! I'll snare every man and woman of your group at the next meeting." And, too, the devil spoke at night in the howling of the wind in the fury of the storm. On calm nights, one could hear the swish of his black wings passing by one's face. How horrible! The devil was even present at meetings. slipping in under the closed door. It was he who made men argue so much and show such hot tempers at their hour of prophesying. It was he who bedevilled the women and made them sit with glazed eyes and tightly closed lips. With the "shadow of the evil one" hovering forever near, many prayers were uttered to guardian angels.

Other superstition was rife. Women were burned as witches for spreading disease. Men were imprisoned for bringing on spells of bitterly cold weather, and even children were beaten for preventing the rain from falling. It was little wonder that people turned to extreme practices to allay fears, such as dancing in the Lord at the Wednesday evening home praise meetings. Had not King David, first King of the Hebrews, danced in the streets of Jerusalem as he joyously led the procession bringing the Ark of the Covenant of the Lord to God's Holy City of Zion? Several men and women would rise and slowly begin to dance, weaving their arms in a wild rhythm. "My tongue is a silent one," someone would say. "It fails to express my praise to the Lord. Yes, my tongue fails, but my feet do not. My feet will sing praise to Him for making the sun, moon and stars to shine upon me. My knees sway and bend in thanking God." Others would follow, as if drawn by a magnet. They would bow to each other, do a few quick steps, a few swift turns and lift their hands very high. It was like a spell coming over the meeting. "My feet are inspired with a great delight," one would call out. "My ankles want to praise the Lord." "My very toes speak with the stars." "My bones are singing to the moon."

"Your bones are devil possessed!" someone would call out in disapproval. "Your feet are heathen feet! Your feet will go to hell!"

"Could my feet go to hell, when my heart flies up to heaven?" the dancer would turn to question. "Why should my big toe burn in hell for wriggling at some tune that pleases the

Lord? The very trees hold conversation with the stars, why then shouldn't my feet speak to God! Judge not and you shall not be judged."

An elderly woman in the congregation would not allow the subject to be dismissed so blithely. "Those dancers! I'll take them before our Council of Elders as evildoers. I may be a mere woman, but I'll do so myself." Protests or not, the dancing continued as single persons and couples whirled about, first slowly, then quickly, then slowly again. Hands fluttered like butterflies. Women's feet kicked so high their white stockings showed. It was shocking that they should enjoy it so much, yet at the same time was it not the release of youthful energy and spirits? Some of the older women onlookers burst into tears, recalling their own youth. What caused these wild storms in the hearts of otherwise quiet people? Was it sinful? Were they brought on by too many hours of endless sermons, the dreadful persecutions, the dangers and hardships they faced day after day? Finally, after many protests, the Council of Elders condemned such frivolity, but the Separatists were an independent lot and dancing in the Lord continued often surreptitiously.

The flock was shepherded by two pastors, Rev. Richard Clyfton and Rev. John Robinson, his assistant. Pastor Clyfton is somewhat bypassed in the annals except for the mention that he was "a worthy man to his flock." Although he was always in favor of anything beneficial to his people, he did not promote such weird ideas as crossing the sea to Holland, let alone the New World, for the sake of religious freedom. John Robinson delighted in serving such fine people, and more than Clyfton, brought the congregation nearer to "ye primitive pattern of ye first church." Married to Bridget White, Robinson had five fine children, John, Bridget, Isaac, Mercy and James. Pastor Robinson was a born preacher, if not exactly a visionary, for he was too inextricably bound up with the pattern of Calvinist dogma and the principles of the Separatists. He delighted in oratory. His manner of speaking was aristocratic and far removed from ordinary loquacity. He could induce a soothing calm in his audience and hold them spellbound by the power of his words for hours, even inducing tears.

It was William Brewster of the Manor House who was destined to be the very soul of the Scrooby movement to Holland and thence to the New World. He, too, was a past master of words which enthralled his listeners. He had learned well at Cambridge and from his association with the well-born, like the Earl of Essex. He loved good literature and stored up precious words to pour out in an abundance of sincerity, enthusiasm and elation which inspired his followers with confidence and hope.

William Bradford, practical, sober, shrewd and solemn, yet had moments when he was almost poet and dreamer, though he controlled these moods as unbefitting a Separatist. He was born on a farm at Austerfield near Scrooby, son of a well-to-do yeoman, and received some schooling. At twelve he began to read the Bible, and soon thereafter William Brewster was instrumental in his conversion to Separatism. In 1606, when the Separatist Church was organized in the Manor House at Scrooby, William Bradford, now 16, joined at once much against the wishes of his apprehensive parents, who had grave reasons to fear for their son's safety. For the following year, when he was one of those who tried to flee from Boston, England, to Holland, he was apprehended and imprisoned for several months. But in 1608 he made a successful attempt, and became one of the first passengers to board a readied Dutch ship, which was blown by a typhoon to the coast of Norway. When the storm subsided, the vessel made its way to the Netherlands.

Matters had reached such an impasse for the Scrooby congregation that efforts were made to seek asylum in Holland for as many as could manage to leave England.

Chapter 2

THE DECISION TO LEAVE ENGLAND

There were many book stores in London by the 17th century. The rich took pride in their libraries of hundreds of costly books, bound in leather and tooled in gold. Illiteracy was the mark of the era. It looked impressive to carry a Bible and hymn book to church and turn the pages. Aided by memory and pictures, one could learn to read a sentence here and there. William Shakespeare was the first of his family to attend school. But now the sons of the rich all went, while the girls remained home to be tutored by their parents in reading, and, less often, writing, since that was reserved for the professional class. Not a household in a thousand in England possessed a sheet of writing paper. Consequently people were indifferent to grammar, and rules were practically unknown. One learned grammatical usage from the clergy, who were university educated, and from the city people. Style of speech was admired by those with high social standing, and their language became the criterion of the land.

Strolling players acted dramas by Shakespeare and his contemporaries. Many players came to the Manor House in Scrooby, but the Separatists considered them unfit for Christian audiences to see. Besides, it seemed unthrifty to spend money for admission to the performances. People should invest any savings with a goldsmith who paid interest regularly; one could use a goldsmith's receipt as a check. There were not

63

many goldsmith-bankers near Scrooby, but one could always invest in mortgages.

Some owned stock in the newly established East Indies Company and had shares in a privateering fleet. These were honorable investments for a Christian and quite profitable. Most of the Separatists had no extra money and rarely used cash. They lived plainly and soberly, without any hopes or dreams of a dramatic change in their lives. They were tenant farmers with no hired help. They rented houses, each with two acres of land, and shared with the owners the crops they raised. From their sheep they gathered wool to card, spin, and weave into cloth for garments, or knit into stockings and warm shawls. Extra work, such as shearing sheep and digging carrots and turnips, they simply shared with each other.

If the farmer was contented, then so was his wife. What if her floors were only covered with rushes against the dirt and cold, were not those of her neighbors similarly covered? What if the only looking-glass in the house were a tiny one kept in her sewing basket beside the spinning wheel, did her neighbors possess larger ones? The farmers had their distractions, too: dinner parties, weddings, funerals. Separatist women loved a wedding. They wept before the ceremony, and the bride wept when her attendants combed her long hair so that it flowed over her shoulders as a symbol of virginity. And the women laughed when they made a garland for her hair of entwined leaves of myrtle, olive and rosemary. Then as the bride shed tears at leaving the home of her parents, her friends cried once more just to show their loving sympathy.

Following the marriage ritual, there was fun for all; dancing at weddings was considered a good Christian custom. After the first dance the newlyweds retired to the flower-decorated bridal chamber to sit demurely side by side on the bed. In between dances, the guests ran in to tease them, make risque jokes and sing boisterous songs until young and old alike dissolved in good-natured laughter. The dancing and singing, teasing and joking kept up until the last of the many wedding guests departed.

When illness befell a family, it was also an occasion for visits. The people were each other's physicians. Each neighbor and friend possessed medicinal herbs and a score of traditional remedies. "A hound's tongue is the best medicine for nausea," one neighbor would say. "Not so," another would reply. "Your pores, sweating so profusely, make you to vomit. Use some marigold and nightshade ground fine and your nausea will be better."

Plague was the most feared of diseases. People still spoke with awe of the dread Black Death which had ravaged England and Europe two centuries before, claiming 25 million victims. Homes in Scrooby with plague were marked with a great red cross and guarded by halberds against entrance. Neighbors and friends made a fumigant of brimstone, saltpeter and tar mixed with juniper berries, cow dung and vinegar to prevent the disease from spreading to their homes. They wore toad amulets and quills around their necks filled with arsenic and quicksilver. Then the town nurse would come and take charge of the house as well as the patient; such was the law. Each town had a group of old, illiterate widows, forced to live apart from society. These pauper women were from the lowest social rung, untrained, and required to carry a white stick to signify their approach so that people could cover their mouths as they passed. Such a nurse had confidence in her treatments even if her remedies were peculiar. She ruled with an iron hand, government-endorsed. She wailed and groaned at the bedside of the patient, closed all windows and kept everyone away. If nothing else helped, she cut a live pigeon in two and tied it to the groin of the sick to drive out the poison.

Wars brought illness and plagues. In days of pestilence, people heard with dread the rumbling of the town cart in the morning, the ringing of the hand bell and the cry of two men: "We have come for your dead! Your dead! Your dead!" People brought out the bodies of their loved ones, which were tossed on the cart for group burials.

Life was hard enough without the extra burden of governmental persecutions. Highly educated people were executed. John Penry, Brewster's classmate at Peterhouse, Cambridge, was hanged at St. Thomas Watering in London; in the spring of 1593 John Greenwood, a contemporary of William Brewster at Cambridge, was executed together with Henry Barrow, one of the great leaders of the early Separation. What was the foundation of this relentless persecution? To destroy all resistance to the regime, the bishops forced a reluctant Parliament to pass the most evil legislation of Queen Elizabeth's long reign, aimed primarily at the Brownists. The law was to be in effect for five years, but was constantly extended until it creeped into the reign of Charles I. It provided that "any person who absented himself from the orthodox services for more than a month or who attempted in any way to persuade others to do so, or who attended any unlawful assemblies, conventicles or meetings under color or pretence of any exercise of religion were to be imprisoned without bail until they pledged themselves to conform. If submission were not made within three months they were to quit the realm on pain of death without benefit of clergy. If they ever returned, they were to be summarily executed."

The death of Queen Elizabeth in 1603 did not rid the country of the malignant evil. James I, first of the Stuarts, continued to work against the reformers. However, the movement for reform presented him promptly with the Millenary Petition, signed by 800 ministers who desired changes in the Anglican Church. This represented one-tenth of the clergy of England seeking relief of the worst of the abuses. James acted on the Petition by calling the Hampton Court Conference early in 1604. It was packed against the petitioners; only four Puritans in all were asked to attend as delegates. They were insulted by the monarch, who acted as chairman of the meeting, and sneered at by the others for their audacity in pleading for liberty of conscience. King James, who established his particular doctrine of the divine right of kings, was adamant against granting such liberty, because then, he reasoned, anyone who wished could censure him and his council. In other words, the demand for freedom of conscience, thought and speech would inevitably lead beyond the field of religion.

James had a personal axe to grind in that he and his mother, Mary Queen of Scots, had been haunted from their cradles by a Puritan devil, he said, so he would suppress the Puritans even if "it costs me my crown." Working himself up into a rage, he broke up the conference with a mighty oath. "I will *make* them conform," he shouted, "or I will harry them out of the land." It was remarkable that something good did come out of the conference, the suggestion of Puritan delegate John Reynolds that a new translation of the Bible be authorized. It was approved, and seven years later the King James Version was published.

Nothing less than the revolution under Oliver Cromwell, which was to cost Charles I his head, could now eliminate the rigidity of the throne toward church reform. James issued new decrees calling for use of the *Book of Common Prayer*, acceptance of the Thirty-Nine Articles, suppression of all private religious meetings, and obligatory communion in the Anglican Church at least three times a year. Failure to comply with these provisions cost three hundred clergymen their posts within a year.

In Scrooby, the Separatists were of the opinion that the Anglican Church was in essence the Catholic Church, and that they, as the Lord's free people in a covenant with God, had joined themselves in a fellowship of the gospel. The final separation from the Anglican Church, in defiance of the law, occurred in 1606 with the arrival in Gainsborough, six miles distant from Scrooby, of John Smyth, graduate of Cambridge, who had been preaching in Lincoln. He was a very able pastor, and people came from Lincolnshire, Nottinghamshire and York-shire to hear him on Sundays. This, indeed, was the first Separatist Congregation. Later it split into two, since the six miles were too far for the Scrooby group to come.

Richard Clyfton, at 50, surrendered his long career in the Anglican Church to join the humble, harrassed Separatists who had been organized by William Brewster and received at the Manor House. John Robinson, a young qualified pastor, one of the 300 clergymen dismissed from the church for nonconformance, joined the congregation. He had been born in the hamlet of Sturton le Steeple and was ten years younger than William Brewster.

In the spring of 1606, the Archbishop held a meeting at the Manor House in Scrooby and ordered a number of the Separatists to be severely punished as a warning to the others. It was a horrifying experience to awaken in the night to the shouts of halberdiers, "Open the door, you Bible worshipper. Open the door in the name of the King and the Church!" The offense was the reading of the Bible in their own homes.

One morning a number of the group met at the Town Square of Scrooby, exchanging silent greetings with their eyes so as not to involve each other. William Brewster had just re-turned from London with the news that the Gainsborough group, which had fled seeking a haven in Holland, had reached Amsterdam safely. The times were so perilous that a daughter born to the Brewsters during this period was named Fear. Brew-ster shocked his listeners when he told of going to London Bridge and seeing rows upon rows of heads rammed onto the pikes. The victims, who had been Puritans, were beheaded for rebellion.

What was there to do in the face of this enveloping horror? "Do?" said Brewster. "There is only one thing we can do—flee for our lives as we are already marked men." The quaint square filled with onlookers. Then the gate of the prison swung open and out marched a number of halberdiers preceded by two officials, each carrying a branding iron, knife and whip. The Bishop and his magistrate, both attired in long black capes, followed, and then, closely surrounded by soldiers, came the prisoners. When the procession reached the roped-off place of punishment, a trumpet sounded from the balcony of the town hall.

"In the name of the King and of the Church!" the halberdiers shouted, and tied the hands of the prisoners behind their backs. The women were stripped to the waist and whipped. The men were shorn of their ears and branded on their foreheads with a B for Bible worshipper. This outrage set the seal on the decision to leave Scrooby.

On September 30, 1607, William Brewster resigned his postmastership under pressure and was brought before the Court of the High Commission on charges of being disobedient in matters of religion. He was very fortunate in escaping with merely a heavy fine—£20.

On the night following the whipping and branding in the Town Square, Pastor Clyfton, Pastor Robinson, Elder Brewster and two deacons went about in the dark to call a meeting, not daring to carry a lighted lantern. They would steal across the blackness of a member's yard and knock at his door by an arranged signal. Inside the house, Brewster would reveal that he had come into possession of secret information from the magistrate that the bishop had instructed the latter to seize and publicly flog at least seven more members at noon the following day.

Brewster warned them that if they insisted upon holding their meetings as a religious observance in lieu of attending services at the Anglican Church, all would be brought to their deaths. "The bishops are now hanging people for just wanting to vote about Church affairs."

"What shall we do? What shall we do?" everyone asked

anxiously, turning for an answer to William Brewster, who replied in low tones, "I know of a place where we could be free to live and to worship—Holland."

"All the way across the North Sea?"

"Yes, I have already been there and I can tell you truly that it is a land of freedom. It would mean our liberation from tyranny and fear. Holland is the country for us."

"We might as well strike our tents. Where could we settle in that strange land with its strange tongue?"

"In Middelburg," Elder Brewster replied convincingly, "right at the coast in the south of Holland. Pastor Browne's congregation went there in 1581. I worshipped there myself in St. Peter's, their own beautiful church."

"You did? And did you understand the service?"

"It was in English," Brewster said.

"Is our language then allowed there for worshipping?"

"Certainly," said Brewster smiling. And in that wonderful continuity of history, today, some 400 years after the original congregation bought the church, the service is still in English.

"Is Middelburg a small town?" asked a man curiously.

"Rather, but we might also go to Amsterdam which is the largest city of Holland. The Ancient Brethren are now living in Amsterdam and so are many Puritans," Brewster continued as he outlined a future home for the group. "Or we could go to the city of Leyden. When I went to that city it seemed to me like a homecoming. How well I remember the very date— January 3, 1586. Our British officers had great worldly luster in their pageantry and elegance, yet before we were dined and wined, the Burgomaster paid homage to God by taking our entire procession to the great St. Peter's Church to offer thanks. Yes, Holland is the place for us to begin new lives, without fear of punishment and death."

A woman bent her head and wept softly, protesting, "But to go away from home, our country of England, our village and our livelihood! How can we ever leave all that is familiar and dear to us? How can we go to a land of strange language and trades which are unknown to us who are farmers and know only husbandry?"

Back and forth they talked, far into the night, about the advisability of leaving Scrooby. It was by no means an easy decision to make. At last they adjourned, agreeing to meet again the following night. They left two by two to avoid arousing any suspicion. Soon dawn came, dew-gray, filmy and wistful in its promise, and wove itself around the low thatched-roof cottage where they had met. It curtained close the little windows with their boxed flowers and swirled through the garden. It stirred the birds into singing of a new day of hope.

At evening, they met in the cellar of the Manor House as a furious rain fell. The wind twisted the branches of the trees as if to break them and added its eerie voice to the deluge. The old mansion cringed, the windows rattled and the night throbbed with gloom. Before they entered the shelter of the house, rain lashed the faces of the men and women and dripped icy cold from the trees in rivulets down their necks—yet they came to the meeting. At intervals, they stopped to peer into the darkness to hear if they were being followed. Do I hear footsteps? Look out! Look out! Do I hear stalking soldiers over there in the distance across the meadow? No, no, it is just the trees rustling in the wind and rain. Danger of detection lurked behind every corner. It was good at last to reach the Manor and descend the flight of stone steps to the cellar in back of the house.

Every precaution was taken against a raid by the Bishop's soldiers. "The place may be searched," William Brewster had warned. "Some of us better sit at the tables and pretend to play cards to outwit the soldiers. If they surprise us, I'll be telling the story of the Manor House in its old days."

The searching question before the gathering was:

Shall we or shall we not go to Holland now?

Pastor Clyfton offered a gloomy reaction. "It is a dear

place and subject to ye miserable wars with Spain. How could we hope to make a living there? Most of you are used only to the innocent trade of husbandry . . . and besides we would have to learn a new language. And there are even greater problems facing us," he continued somberly. "The law forbids us to leave England without permission of the Crown. We will have to get away like thieves in the night. And that to a country which does not even keep the right calendar."

Everyone raised an eyebrow questioningly. "What calendar?"

"Our good, old Julian one. The Dutch have abandoned it and have accepted the Gregorian calendar. Pope Gregory XII, who was interested in scientific things, proposed a change in the calendar, explaining that since the days of Julius Caesar, it had been at variance with the movements of the sun. You see, our Julian year consists of three hundred and sixty-five and one-quarter days. The Pope, who said there was an error of calculation, proposed in 1582 to rectify the fault by doing away with ten days. Thus the 5th of December in the year of 1582 became the 15th of December. All Catholic countries corrected their calendars in accordance with the Papal instructions. Even Holland for purely scientific reasons, so they say, but Britain refused to do so and kept the old calendar."

It is a fact that for a long, long time to come the Pilgrims kept double dates. They headed all of their letters from Holland with two dates. Germany conformed to the new solar reckoning in 1700, England in 1746 and Sweden in 1753. Russia clung to the chronological error until as late as 1920.

As they discussed the vagaries of the calendar, they were startled by the noise of boots on the stairs and then fierce hammering at the door, demanding entry in the name of the King. The Bishop's soldiers raided the Manor House cellar meeting on May 20, 1608.

Half expecting trouble, William Brewster ordered, "Start playing cards! Stay calm!"

He went to the door and opened it. "If it is beer you want, you are mistaken. Beer is sold upstairs, not here. I am telling the history of the Manor House to some friends tonight. Do come in and stay."

The surprised soldiers entered the room and indeed saw the cards and the players, but there were no Bibles nor hymn books anywhere. It was not a meeting of worship, after all, but only a neighborly gathering. Unconvinced, they remained to listen to Brewster's story about the Manor House. It held many memories for him personally, coming as he did to live in the rambling old mansion as a lad of ten, going forth at 15 to attend Cambridge, and to Holland in the service of the Court, marrying there [either late in 1591 or early in 1592] his lovely wife Mary [possibly the daughter of Thomas Wentworth, whom William Brewster, Sr. had succeeded as Bailiff-Receiver of Scrooby Manor.] Then he unwound the story of visiting royalty, and the soldiers listened raptly in spite of themselves. Oh, he was a magician with words, and soon they rose and left, perhaps a bit reluctantly, as it seemed so pleasant there in the warmth of human companionship.

Finally the gathering dispersed in little groups of two and three, but not before they had definitely decided on emigration from England. They would, they pledged, dispose of their property secretly, their farm animals and holdings, and leave for Holland just as soon as the harvest had been gathered and sold. That very night the soldiers took seven of their group into custody. It was a mystery how the Bishop learned about their decision so secretly arrived at. Day by day he ordered more of the Separatists jailed in narrow cells with thin straw on stone floors. Infected with jail fever, they suffered untold misery, and had no money to buy extra food above the poor fare the jailer brought to them. They had no friends of influence to plead their cause. They ate bitterness, but took courage from the wind of change that was in the air. The Lord sifted and winnowed in His wondrous ways His miracles to perform, for His Kingdom might truly come first on the continent. Was New England not predestined? And was that why the Lord pushed them to go on to Holland? Were they, indeed, a chosen people, people set apart to perform a great task in the vineyard of the Lord?

That summer they secretly sold their homes and furniture, cows and sheep and other livestock, and the proceeds of their harvest. When September began to color the sunsets a sweet amethyst, they had already hidden away the money under the thatch of the roof, behind a loose brick in the well, or under a pile of peat for the fireplace—wherever the searchers might fail to look. In October, when they were financially in position to hire passage on a ship, they assigned Brewster to bargain secretly with a shipmaster to take 60 of them on board. Since all ports and havens were shut against them by ordinance of the Bishop, they were compelled to seek surreptitious means of conveyance, giving bribes and fees to mariners, and to pay extraordinary rates for their passage to Holland.

William Brewster went by horseback to Boston, on the Wash, an inlet, to hire a ship to accommodate only their own group, with no other passengers, since they were a considerable comapny. After much negotiation, the contract for transportation was signed with an English shipmaster. They lost little time in departing. Most of them set out on foot in the black of the night to traverse the 60 miles southeast to Boston to meet the hired vessel. The older women and small children rode on open carts with piles of clothing, keepsakes and a supply of baked beans, large cheeses and loaves of rye bread for the journey and voyage. The younger women and older children walked with the men the long distance between Scrooby and Boston. Finally there rose before their eyes the famous tall tower of the ancient St. Botolph Church, renowned as the Boston Stump. It was a welcome sight, yet they feared to enter the city, to risk detection and apprehension. William Brewster went directly to ask the Captain to take them on board without undue delay.

This would be impossible, and he returned in disappointment to report that men would come soon for their baggage, but the group would have to wait until the Captain's order came for them to go on board. It meant spending another night wherever they could find some kind of makeshift accommodation. Some of the men found an inn for their wives and the younger children, and at last all had secured some kind of sleeping place. However, it was not to be a night of rest after the weary journey, for a few hours after they had retired, Elder Brewster came knocking at the door of the inn with the order, "Awake! Awake! The Captain has sent me word that we must come at once!"

Dressing in haste, they left the inn and the other lodgings with their belongings and went straight to the ship, which lay hidden in a cove outside of the harbor. Quietly they got into the shallops which had been sent for them, but hardly had they reached the ship and climbed the rope-ladder up to the deck, when someone cried out in terror, "The soldiers! The soldiers! They are coming here for us!"

What was the meaning of this? After signing a contract with Elder Brewster, accepting passage money for the group and making all of the necessary arrangements, it was incredible that the Captain would commit such villainy. Yet it was true. The faithless shipmaster had notified the Bishop's men of the embarkation of the Separatists, constituting an illegal attempt to leave England. It was not out of patriotism that he betrayed them, but greed, for the money he had received for the fares he divided among the soldiers and his first mate. The soldiers, hidden in the hold of the ship, now sprang forward and rifled the defenseless passengers, searching even down to the underwear of both men and women for concealed money. They searched inside the linings of their cloaks and waistcoats and robbed them of whatever they had, then ordered them off the ship. "Down the rope-ladder! Back into the shallops, all of you!" the soldiers shouted.

His eyes blazing with anger, Brewster called out to the English Captain, "You scoundrel, you have betrayed us!" but, as a confirmed believer in non-violence, he refrained from assaulting him. He descended the ladder and got into a shallop with the others, who sat huddled immobile in the little boats. They slouched disconsolately on the low benches, their heads sunk between their hunched shoulders in utter misery and profound disappointment at the swift turn of events which ruined months of careful planning and meant financial disaster.

"Where are we being taken to?" Brewster asked.

"Back to Boston," an officer replied. "Hold on to your clothes boxes. All of you! Pile your bundles close beside you."

In the darkness of a moonless night, a woman asked without much purpose, "What time is it?"

"After one."

Although it was very late, people had flocked from all sides to the harbor to watch the return of the captives and to taunt them. "You Bible worshippers . . . You stiff-necked Separatists! You deserve to be punished for withdrawing from our Anglican Church."

So they were paraded as a spectacle for the crowd. How queer they were in their somber clothes, trying to leave their homeland in the still of the night for another country because of freedom of worship. For some it was a first experience in being publicly abused, railed at and ridiculed. This scoffing continued all the way to the Boston jail, where they were pushed into cells too small to accommodate so many, and were retained for a month. Some had to sit on the floor and, since there was no room for all of them to lie down during the night, they had to take turns. There were tears for their lost hope and their present misery until one of the men said, "Don't water the roots of your hope with tears. Where they fall, nothing will grow, nor bloom, nor bear fruit. Take your portion of happiness, however small, without pushing, planning, striving, and enlarge upon it. Don't let the hardness of these bricks, the dampness of the straw, nor the discomfort detract you from your joy. Open your eyes wide, look through the bars of yon tiny window. If you can't see the sun, look at the colors in the sky and take that glow as your portion of the happiness of this day."

After a month, the group was released except for Brewster, Clyfton, Robinson, William Bradford and three others, held for trial. At last an exhausted group straggled back to Scrooby and the other villages, and a few weeks later, the seven who had been detained in Boston also returned. They had been punished not only for reading the Bible and explaining it as they understood it, but for not adhering to the Anglican Church of the crown, since this was required by law of all people of the realm. Thereafter, anyone who attended the Separatist meetings was treated as a heretic, a mocker, a scorner, a criminal—"a rat to be trapped and tossed away" as King James commanded.

It was a bitter winter of dire poverty. Cupboards were bare in many homes; cows, goats and pigs had been sold for the ship passage. Still beneath the snow, life was taking on a new form, and before long spring came with its gentle promise. One may always hope, if only there is courage to maintain it. During the spring of 1608, William Brewster met at Hull a Christian Dutch sea captain with a ship of his own sailing for Zealand, the southern province of the Netherlands. Trusting that he would be faithful, Brewster revealed their circumstances and made a contract with him for the group to be taken onto his ship, between Grimsby and Hull, at a creek which was the farthest shipping point between the two towns.

Brewster hastily returned to Scrooby to bring the good news to his family and friends. That very night they all left in haste and secrecy, the women by boat, the men walking overland in scattered groups, carefully avoiding all towns and country constables. At parting, the men told the women, "Whatever trouble arises, stay on the boat. If you arrive at our destination before we do, wait for us in the bark."

Many prayers were said that this time they would be successful in making their escape from England. Yet much trial and tribulation were in store for them before they would set foot on the firm land of Holland.

Chapter 3

TO MIDDELBURG, THE NETHERLANDS

It was a rendezvous of great moment and high expectations at Hull, where a second attempt would be made to sail from England. In the dimness of the night, the women and younger children glided gently in their small boat from the Idle River to the Trent and thence to the Humber River. When they reached the open sea a blustering wind arose, which drove the sail boat forward at full speed, so that they arrived at the place of meeting a day ahead of schedule. The arrangements were that they would wait for the men to arrive. Many of the women had become seasick and begged the owner of the bark to anchor in the creek so they could sleep; they could not stand the tossing about of the rough sea any longer.

"No, no! The soldiers might find you," he warned.

"The Dutch ship isn't arriving until tomorrow morning, so you might as well anchor there," a woman said quite reasonably. There was no use remonstrating with the pleading women any longer, so the boatmen ordered the bark to proceed to the cove. The next morning, he found to his disgust that the boat was aground and could not move. He blamed himself for acting contrary to his mariner's good judgment. "It won't float free until noon brings in the high tide. What am I to do?" he asked in bewilderment.

At this moment the Dutch ship arrived and its Captain watched in astonishment as the crew walked about on shore as if there were not the slightest danger of detection. "Send ye rowboat," he ordered the crew, "to be getting ye men aboard. And send another boat for the women and children and be quick about it. Row back for more as fast as ye can!" A faithful man, he wanted to keep his part of the contract to evacuate the harassed Separatists. Twice they went out and brought in as many as the boat would hold. Among others there was William Brewster and William Bradford, a lad of 18. The boatman was ready to get the remaining people when suddenly a great company arrived on horseback and on foot, shouting their protest against English men, women and children leaving their homeland in an unlawful manner in defiance of the King and Church.

The Dutch Captain immediately gave orders to weigh anchor and to hoist the sails in a quick departure. From the ship moving toward the sea, they saw some of the men on shore run from the docks while others who tarried were taken into custody by the soldiers. As the wind billowed the sails, the ship was soon safely out of range of the guns, but those on board wept piteously for loved ones left behind. In the confusion and haste of embarkation, many boxes and bundles were not put on board. Many children were separated from parents and wives from husbands.

As the passenger ship sailed away, the Bishop's soldiers surrounded the little boarding shallop which lay aground and aimed their guns at the defenseless women and children who had not been fortunate enough to board the vessel in time. They forced them to wade through the shallow water and form a group with the men on shore. Then they were marched to the town hall of Boston and brought before the magistrate, who was puzzled as to what action to take to provide maintenance for such a large number of people who had been left without funds. Since the law moved very slowly, they would have to be housed and fed for weeks before disposition could be made of their case. The charge was an attempt at unauthorized exit from England.

Since the town jail was so small, the official sent a few at a time under guard to various residents, but they refused to quarter the prisoners. The magistrate then shifted the accused from one judge to another and from town to town, but no one wanted their custody. Meanwhile the group received little or no food and haphazard sleeping accommodations. All the magistrates were perplexed as to how to handle the case. According to English law, the wives who had been caught before boarding the ship were blameless, because they were supposed to follow their husbands. Therefore they had not committed a crime nor had the children, who should legitimately follow their fathers.

The magistrate after several weeks grew tired of the vexing problem of the women and children and set them free, glad to be rid of them. They wandered about, seeking means whereby they could buy passage to Holland to join their husbands. Their peculiar plight aroused a natural sympathy, and many found kind people willing to help them with food and money, so that the more fortunate were able to sail for Holland, exhausted but happy. The men prisoners, however, were retained as long as their money lasted to pay for their keep, then the magistrate also let them leave. Some men found their way to Holland, but others gave up hope of leaving the country and had to remain in England.

Meanwhile those on the Dutch ship were troubled; many had been separated from their relatives and the voyage was very rough. A squall turned into a violent storm and waves poured across the deck. The wind was already biting into their bones, and most of them had no bedding nor extra dry or warm clothing. How, pray, were they going to sleep? Somehow they managed, but the next day the storm did not subside, turning into a gale, then a hurricane. There was nothing for the Captain to do but run before it and trust to Divine Providence. The vessel was tossed about like a cork, its compass useless. The driving rain made it impossible for anyone to see where they were. They were lost at sea and completely off course. Stormy days of hunger and abject misery ran into each other; salt water soaked their clothing and chilled them. Many were frightfully seasick as enormous waves lifted the small ship up and hurled it down again. Even the crew were worried about their fate.

For seven days wild sea, heavy squalls and blinding rain threatened to tear the ship apart. But their doom really seemed sealed on the evening of the seventh day when some sailors on deck cried out, "We are sinking! Our ship is lost!" The buffeted passengers gathered in a knot on the rolling, wet and windswept deck and knelt in prayer. Was not the Lord with them? Could not He bid the sea to be quiet as His son had commanded at Galilee? And as they prayed, the miracle came. The mortal storm had spent itself. The darkness lifted and a coastline appeared dimly before their eyes.

"Ah, but it is the coast of Norway!" the wearied Captain told them disappointedly. "As you prayed, I watched as it became more and more visible."

Norway! They had been swept at least four hundred miles due north out of their course. "Steer back, Captain! Steer us back to Holland!" they cried out in chorus, "for that is where we want to go."

Two days later, to the great excitement of the passengers, their ship arrived at the harbor of Flushing, near Middelburg, where some people had come to the coast as soon as they sighted the ship. Among them were a number of Separatists living in Holland, who could be recognized even from afar by their somber clothing. One of the first visitors to come on board was the wife of the Rev. Francis Johnson, the English Pastor of the Puritan Church. In a friendly gesture, she tucked a tiny bunch of daffodils into the belt of Mrs. Brewster, who, although touched by the friendliness, was shocked. Imagine a Christian woman decorating herself with flowers! But it was pagan! Mrs. Johnson seemed not to notice any of the consternation she had created by her welcome, and cheerfully told Mary Brewster that homes had been found for many of them with members of the

Dutch Reformed Church, who were friendly to the Puritans and Separatists. The Brewsters and their sons Love and Wrestling were lodged in a home in the Gravenstraat, Earl Street. So were John Carver and his wife Catherine and their daughter Desire and young William Bradford.

As they walked toward their lodging place, they noticed some interesting looking signs. It was an old Dutch custom for owners of homes to give them a name, which was indicated above the door by a pictured signboard of the trade or profession of the proprietor, so that newcomers could easily find their way about. They let their eyes dart from the weather vane of one steep roofed house to the turret of another. They watched a woman of quality riding in a leather-topped coach and peasants in native costume greeting each other with a raised finger.

The Captain, for his part, had generously invited as many of the voyagers to stay in his home as his wife could provide beds for, or space on the floor for sleeping on straw. "The rest will find friendly homes of the Dutch and English people opened up to you," he reassured them, and proceeded to send them here and there for shelter.

The English were so excited upon their arrival, they could barely restrain themselves. Now they were truly in another country. There were many reunions of families and friends. New ways were everywhere in evidence. It was pleasant to use the large bronze door knockers, and to enter rooms with floors of gleaming white and black flagstones, to warm themselves at a large fireplace glowing with a friendly peat fire, for there is no fuel more cozy than damp wood and frozen peat. Such wood always sings and the peat murmurs as it listens. Some of the homes were unpretentious, while others were luxurious, with Persian rugs covering the tables, oil paintings on the walls, ebony-framed mirrors between windows; many beautiful objects of Delft blue porcelain and show plates of blue hung on the walls of the staircases. Of curious interest were the Latin mottoes in the tiles of the fireplaces.

Their first evening in Holland, they enjoyed a wonderful meal, so skillfully offered by the Dutch. Relieved to be able to retire at last, some had to sleep on makeshift beds on the floor, as there were not enough beds for all. Others were brought to large, high-ceilinged bedrooms. When they disrobed, each guest placed his or her clothes in the traditional strong box carved with biblical scenes which was placed beside the bed, and climbed three steps up a little wooden stool into the allotted sleeping cupboard, to sink into the softness of the traditional feather mattress so beloved by Europeans. Some did not sleep too well that night because Tall John and Silly Beth, Lange Jan en Gekke Betje, kept calling to them every seven and a half minutes. The wakeful ones would, the first few times, peer apprenehsively into the darkness of their rooms to determine what were those wistful sighs, plaintive airs, and softly echoing bell tones.

Unable to restrain his curiosity, William Bradford got up, fumbled for the firestone and flint lying on the bedside table, and lighted his candle. He instinctively watched the large wall clock and waited for those bells to sound. They did faithfully, eight times in an hour, but it was not the clock but from outdoors. Listening, he grew drowsy, blew out his candle and returned to bed.

The next morning young Bradford complained, "Those chimes, ringing all night long . . . chimes and more chimes . . . where do they come from?"

"From Lange Jan en Gekke Betje, the carillon in the Abbey Tower and the Town Hall clock. They play day and night. I hope they didn't keep you awake."

Enjoying his plovers' eggs, kievits eieren, the special Zeeland treat for honored guests, he assured his host to the contrary.

"You see silly Beth is in love with tall John," his host explained, "and whenever his voice rings out in peals of chimes, she answers in whispers of ecstasy."

"Could we see them? How we wish we could see them," the Brewster children, Love and Wrestling, asked almost in unison. "Could we really?" Desire Carter added her plea.

So, naturally curious about the charms of the city of Middelburg, many toured the old place the first morning after their arrival. As their baggage had not yet come, and the weather was cool, the Brewsters and Carvers were offered the loan of coats and cloaks, which made for a small problem, since the Dutch people dressed more colorfully than the Separatists thought proper. One of the handsome cloaks offered the women was of Burgundian red velvet, set off with a beautiful dark fur. The men felt it their duty to express at least a half-hearted objection to such finery, but the warmhearted cordiality of their Dutch hosts sealed the husbands' lips.

Reading their minds, their host explained, "We like radiant colors. People from so many countries come to our city, and there are so many different customs here, that our city is like a museum. But come now, you had better begin your sightseeing at once, as there is a great deal you will wish to see before the midday meal."

The English realized how important it was to adhere to their own ways of attire; otherwise they could easily lose their identity. The Dutch had a winning, persuasive way about them they found hard to resist. Now they would enjoy becoming acquainted with the new city. The street life of Middelburg fascinated them. The steep gables of the houses and their red and black shutters seemed so different. A distant milk cart, its shining brass cans glittering in the sun, was pulled along by two large dogs. They watched three smiling peasant women with their arms linked to each other come swinging along the street, the short sleeves of their black bodices so tight their upper arms took on a ruddy hue, their lace caps snow white, and their cheeks blooming as rosy as apples. The woman at the end held a boy of five years by the hands. He looked like a man in miniature, the custom being to dress children the same as their parents.

"Oh, look! Look!" Mary Brewster said delightedly. "Dressed exactly like his father with black trousers, a tight black velvet jacket, silver belt buttons and gold neck links. Even his tight black hat is like a man's. A little Dutchman bursting through black velvet!"

"And, look over there!" her sister interrupted. "Farmers riding in a wagon. It isn't a coach, but it has a canvas top to keep out sun and rain."

In England, only nobles and wealthy merchants drove in a coach; the laborer always went on foot. It had been so ordained by the Lord. To offer an English peasant a ride to shelter him from the rain would never have occurred to a coachman. It simply was not done. That was the way of the times. Each caste remained to its own—noble, gentry, yeoman, feudal servant, peasant. Birth determined all, and the line was seldom if ever crossed. As a child the nobleman learned from his grandfather and his church that it was his right to be driven in a barouche, coach or carriage. From his days in the wooden box which served as his cradle, the peasant was told by his grandfather and church that he was expected to be foot folks. So it had always been, even in Holland.

It is strange, as are many things in history, that the humble herring played a part in changing the caste system to a great extent. In the 12th century, the herring moved its habitat from the Baltic Sea into the North Sea off Holland. For some time the Dutch did not know how to exploit these fish, and so the potential industry and its wealth was lost. One day, it is said, a young fisherman brought a barrel of North Sea herring, thoroughly salted, to his bride as a practical joke, to see her utter chagrin at the inedible fish, but to his amusement and amazement their dinner guests found the salted herring delicious. The young husband had accidentally invented an easy way to preserve them. Herring now proved to be very profitable, since the larger part of the world outside of Holland observed the Catholic non-meat diet on Friday and fast days, and strict Catholics in southern Europe often went without meat for half of each week. Thus salted herring became a welcome addition to the table. Soon, as the entire continent began eating Dutch herring, fishermen and peasants became affluent, and even though preachers scolded them from the pulpit by calling them "democrats", considered a derogatory term, the Dutch working man kept right on bettering his living standards. He decided to put a stop to walking when he could afford to avail himself of a wagon, against all the old traditions of "foot folks."

All these changes came as a surprise to the newly arrived English, who imagined that Holland was a country of people in baggy trousers and wooden shoes, a country of windmills and canals. They had no idea that the Dutch laborers were more independent than those of any other nation. Middelburg was certainly a charming city—even as it is today—serene, happy, warmly human, built around the Abbey, the Abbey of St. Nicholas. The entire town is in the round. Even the streets curve, quite in keeping with the nature of the people, who smile roundly and appear to live roundly.

"I don't understand how Dutch Calvinists can take pleasure in wearing ostrich plumes and golden gloves," Bradford observed to Brewster as he watched the passersby. "Are the Dutch truly religious?"

"Are the Dutch religious? They may not be ascetic like us, but I can assure you that their religion is vital and very much their own. Why, the very street we are walking on testifies to it. Do you see that large mansion over there? When in 1506 King Charles V returned from residence there to Spain, he believed he could bring the Dutch people back into the Roman Catholic fold, but three years later, King Philip I, his successor, was forced to flee from that same royal residence. These two Spanish monarchs and their invading armies massacred thousands of the Dutch people and burned their lovely cities, but still the Dutch refused to surrender their freedom of religion."

Distressed at the serious vein of the men's conversation, Catherine Carver hastily changed the subject. "It surprises me," she said, "to see so many dark-haired people here. I thought they would all be fair-haired and fair-complexioned and have blue eyes."

"In the north there live the tall, fair, reticent Frisians," Brewster said. "In the south there are the dark, exuberantly warm-hearted inhabitants of Zeeland. Ethnically the Dutch are variable, because the earliest known inhabitants were the Celts, who soon were absorbed by the Frisians, Saxons, and Franks. While the fair haired Saxons dominated the north, the dark complexioned Franks settled in the south, and their differences can be seen in their type and stature as well as language."

"What are those people doing in front of that cloister?" Mary Brewster asked one of the Dutch women who was accompanying them.

"Buying at the butermarkt—butter market."

Housewives moved from one roll of butter displayed on the counters to another. They patted the butter with a flat ladle, plunged a tiny scoop into it and removed a little, which they smelled and tasted. Turning away from the butter market, the party entered a narrow street made almost impassable by a huge shop sign of wood swinging overhead and a red striped barber's pole with two copper basins jingling against each other in the breeze. Street calls in Dutch puzzled the English.

"What is that man asking for his eggs?" Mary Brewster said.

"Five cents for thirty eggs."

"Only thirty!" Mary Allerton said in disgust. "I knew that this would be an expensive country to live in."

Mary Brewster's eyes now found a door-knocker decorated with ribbons, thyme and eglantine, and a little basket was on the stoop—steps. "What does it mean?" she wondered curiously.

"The basket? Oh, that is a luierk or—layette. It announces the birth of a baby."

Some of the women hurried over to inspect the dainty basket. Others were more attracted by a maid who trundled a water pump out of a house and sprayed a pail of water against the house front. It was astounding to see someone keeping a home clean on the outside as well as on the inside.

"I believe they even shine the brass hoops," one remarked, looking at the shining wires of the wooden pail.

"All those big homes!" John Carver exclaimed in admiration. "Holland must be a very prosperous country indeed."

When the Separatists found themselves in Holland, they felt like other Europeans must have when experiencing the effects of the Renaissance, the revival of letters, arts and science which marked the transition from medieval to modern history. It began in Italy and gradually spread and developed in other countries from the 15th to the 17th centuries.

The Netherlands is bounded on the west and north by the North Sea and on the east by Germany; on the south by Belgium. It has almost a perfect climate, with mild winters and moderately warm summers, influenced by the Gulf Stream, which gives the land an average of 34° in January and 64° in July.

"I wonder," said John Carver, "why they call it Holland."

"Well," answered William Brewster from his fund of knowledge, "the word Holland first appeared in the tenth century and is believed to have come from the word Holtland, meaning woodland. Originally this was applied to a region around Leyden, but later to the Province of Holland, which is the most important of the seven United Provinces of the Netherlands which were formed in 1579."

John Carver paused a moment, then asked, "Didn't Robert Browne settle here in Middelburg around that time?"

"Oh, yes," Brewster rejoined. "He came to this city in 1582. Browne was 30 years old when I was studying at Cambridge, and I recall his followers becoming known as Brownists. After he was jailed by the Bishop, he escaped to Holland and blazed the trail for the rest of us to follow. He published two works in Middelburg shortly after coming here, a treatise on the Reformation and a book on the life and manner of the true Christian."

"Would you say he rejected John Calvin's precepts?"

"Yes," explained Brewster, "he, Browne, refused to believe that reform of the church had to wait until the state took action. Browne held that the kingdom of God was to be begun by a few souls who were worthy within a parish, who would find the strength to secede or separate from the established church."

"I think Browne lived in Norwich in England," recalled John Carver, warming to their discussion. "It was a Puritan center where there were Dutch Mennonites. They came to live there as workers in the woolen trade, and I'm sure Browne imbibed some of their ideas."

"The Mennonites," added Brewster, "are members of the Protestant denomination that grew out of the Anabaptist movement in the 16th century. You know, they were the people opposed to the baptizing of infants. Their leader, Menno Simmons, was born the year Columbus discovered America, and if I remember correctly, I read he died about 1559. The Mennonites are opposed to taking oaths, too, to military service and to theological learning."

"Of course they believe in the democracy of the congregation," said Carver. "They selected their own pastor and officers and were the first to call the true believers 'saints' whose lives and acts had to be continually searched and reviewed. But human beings, as you know, resent others sitting in judgment on them, and that is what broke up Browne's church."

"Yes," said Brewster, "when Browne returned to England, he denounced his own creation, turned away from the congregation, and made his peace with the Catholic Bishop."

"I am happy to be here now in Holland," concluded John Carver. "Just think how much we have suffered to leave our homeland in England, and what trials lie in wait for us to endure."

"But be of good cheer," said Brewster. "Consider how much better off we are to be beginning a new life here. I recall with sadness my dead friends. There was John Penry, whom I knew at Cambridge. He was destined for the gallows, and John Greenwood of Corpus Christie, who met the same fate for his non-conformity. John Udall, that brilliant student at Trinity, was condemned to death in 1588, but the sentence was not executed. However, he died in prison four years later."

What was not generally known, but what every crowned head in Europe realized, was that the religious rebellions and the civil wars they provoked were a general conflict under the guise of religion. They represented a crisis of social, political and economic significance as the old feudal order—based on the principle of the landed and the landless—was disintegrating along with its caste system, restrictions on trade and manufacturing, and its antiquated fiscal methods.

When the Separatists of Scrooby and its environs sought a haven in Holland, this country was indeed in its Golden Age. The peasants, the foot folks, the common people, had moved away from their settlements around castle and burg. They began to search for work. People from other countries also walked about in the Dutch towns, as well as seamen from unknown ports. People in the early 17th century were interested in travel; the high road no longer belonged to robber and the sea to pirates. New lands, new oceans, new waters were being discovered everywhere. Nations laid claim to world-wide power. England began to take possession of the New World, as Holland laid claim to the East Indies.

Colonialism meant large investments, which made many people rich quickly. Bankers, investing in the newly discovered lands of the New World, began to live in a princely fashion.

The new prosperity was reflected in the homes wealthy people constructed and furnished lavishly. They were large and strongly built, aimed at lasting for generations of the families their owners proudly founded. Mansions became the style as the residence of merchants; formerly such expensive homes belonged only to the nobility. Now mansions of the mercantile princes boasted private ballrooms whose walls were richly lined in satin, and social entertainments were on a grandiose scale.

It was only natural for the newcomers to be pleased with the city and country of Holland. However, the jovial social ways of the gay Hollanders met with their disapproval. Here was a group of strolling players, and there a juggler, giving a sample of his skill, pranced down a street. Dutch boys and girls on their way to an entertainment were so elegantly attired, with sweeping ostrich plumes on the young men's hats over well curled locks, and wore such handsome, velvet breeches! The sleeves of the girls' dresses were slashed to show the fabric of rich silken undergarments. The girls' bonnets were dainty and laden with lace, which also trimmed the necklines of their dresses. Street life in general pleasantly resembled that of the towns of England, with its animation, street vendors and cries.

The Puritans of England had good reason to oppose the "gay apparel" of the clerics by adopting somber dress for their sect. The Catholic Bishops lived in excessive luxury and personal indulgence, in food, comfort and attire. On his travels the Archbishop of Canterbury used large troops of white horses and hundreds of attendants resplendent in scarlet livery and gold braid, bedecked with solid gold chains. Even highly placed nobles were Puritans, such as the Earl of Leicester, Queen Elizabeth's young favorite, and also the 16th century poets Edmund Spenser, renowned for his *Faerie Queen*, and Sir Philip Sidney, popular courtier, soldier, author, and model of unselfish chivalry.

William Brewster, who, more than any other man can be considered the leader of the Pilgrim movement to Holland and later to the New World, was himself the son of a gentleman, since his father William Brewster, had been commissioned as Bailiff at Scrooby in 1575 by Archbishop Grindal of York, who later became Archbishop of Canterbury. The Brewster family was both recognized and helped by prominent clergymen in the Anglican Church. Archbishop Grindal was succeeded by Edwin Sandys, who as first Dean of York Cathedral distributed land leases in the Scrooby-Nottinghamshire, area to members of his own family, granting each of his six sons large blocks of church property. It so happened that Scrooby Manor went to his second son, later Sir Samuel. The sons of Edwin Sandys performed many good offices in behalf of the Separatists or Pilgrims. Even after almost four centuries, Scrooby Manor lands still remain in the hands of Sir Samuel's heirs and assigns.

But let us return to the group of Englishmen as they become acquainted with the city of their Dutch hosts. Their first midday meal in Middelburg was enjoyed close to a comfortable peat fire: a bowl of bread pudding, slices of cured ham, and a dish of pork and beans. The haunch of ham was removed from a hook in the fireplace, some slices cut off and eaten with the fingers, and bread. As in England, the spoon was used for soups and gruel—stews—while other foods were handled with the fingers. Only the wealthy or those at court had forks. Beer was the general Dutch beverage, and water, as everywhere else, was held in disdain.

After the meal, the men enjoyed smoking their clay pipes. William Brewster lost little time in writing a letter to English friends in Amsterdam. His goose quill pen glided over the paper with the familiar scratching sound; then he sprinkled a little white sand on the paper, enclosed the letter in an envelope and carefully sealed it with melted wax.

"I'll attend to the letter right away," their host said. Pulling the bell rope in the corner of the sitting room, he said to the manservant who quickly appeared, "See to it that this letter is sent off with the first trekshuit—towboat."

On Sunday morning at seven, the Dutch family gathered around the breakfast table in their colorful holiday attire which contrasted with the dull gray and blacks the English wore to symbolize their disdain for Anglican pomp and splendor. The mistress of the house appeared at breakfast in her hood of light blue satin, folded back to reveal carefully tended blonde curls, and highlighting her darker blue velvet dress which was accented with little satin ribbon bows. To match his lady, the master of the house was a picture of sartorial elegance. A fluffy white lace ruffle was around his throat, a yellow satin coat was set off by puffed brown velvet breeches caught with velvet ribbons at the knees above elegantly dressed legs in white silk stockings. The young son and heir of the family appeared, attired as finely, and gracefully placed his gold topped cane and gloves with golden cuffs on a nearby richly upholstered chair.

"Desire, please pull your hood further down. Your forehead shows too much," Mrs. Carver said to her little daughter in rightful indignation over so much worldliness displayed in an allegedly godly family. But Desire didn't even hear her mother's order, so absorbed was she in observing the young Dutchman come to table. She noted that his handsomely made boots came up over his knees, where the soft polished leather folded down in magnificently crinkly cuffs. As he sat down to his breakfast, he straightened, with a careless gesture, the gold stripes at the side of his breeches, and adjusted his satin coat enhanced with embroided golden flowers.

"In England we never wear velvet or satin clothes to church," young William Bradford observed mildly enough.

"I know, I know," their genial host said in all good humor. "I have seen Puritans and Separatists come to our country before, and the Brownists have been in Middelburg for a long time. As a matter of fact, Pastor Robert Browne came to our city with a part of his congregation as early as 1581. When he returned to England the following year, many of his church members remained here, and in 1596 some removed to Amsterdam, but a few still live here. At first they, too, were critical of our colorful clothes but in time they changed their disapproving attitude and they soon learned to be more tolerant. This morning in church you will see for yourself that they have begun to dress more like us Hollanders. You know, I serve as an Elder in our Dutch Reformed Church," he added.

An Elder! Young John Robinson, still inextricably bound up within the strict pattern of Pilgrim behavior, was appalled to see before him an Elder in puffed brown velvet breeches with ribbons around his knees.

"Our religious convictions are much the same as yours, John," said the Elder reading young Robinson's mind. "We, too, believe in a church founded upon the Holy Scriptures. We tolerate neither popes, bishops, nor the ritual of wine and bread made into the blood and body of Jesus Christ. However, I must admit that I do like a bit of color in my clothing. You may prefer a starched flat collar around your neck, and I a ruffled one of starched lace."

It was said in all friendliness and reasonableness, as one countryman familiar with certain ways to a traveler from another country whose ways differed. They went to church in a little group that first Sunday morning in Middelburg, a bit awe-struck by the strangeness of their surroundings, not understanding the language, noting the strange manners and strange dress. Would they ever become accustomed to all of it?

Mary Brewster paused for a moment to look at a wooden sign suspended in front of a house. It depicted a tree bearing ripe fruit. But how fairy-like and whimsical! A luscious pinkly nude infant represented each piece of fruit, and beneath the painted tree stood an ample woman holding wide her large apron, entreating the little ones to jump down from the branches into it.

"That's the sign of a midwife," the Dutch woman laughingly explained in her tutored English. "Ours is a religious land. See for yourself, all the shops are shuttered and gambling on Sunday is forbidden by law."

"Not in England," young John Robinson said. As he spoke, his glance darted into an alley. A circle of men appeared throwing coppers onto the ground. They were betting on the agility of two young fellows who were trying to knock each other's hat off. He peered slyly at his hostess. No, she had not noticed this lapse of religious fervor, illegal betting on Sunday. To divert her attention, he began to talk rapidly about their lives in Scrooby, England.

The ancient small stone church, where the English Puritans met, presented a rather pleasant surprise to the Pilgrims. Lace-like in architecture, it had blue stained-glass windows which gave it a brilliance too worldly beautiful for the Pilgrim's taste, very similar to the breathtaking blue windows of the 12th-century Notre Dame Cathedral in Paris, long familiar to traveling Hollanders. The wife of Pastor Johnson came graciously forward to welcome them.

"It is wonderful to worship in an English congregation on the first Sunday of my arrival," Mary Brewster said. "I can hardly wait to praise the Lord in song."

"Oh, my dear, I hope you won't try to sing! One of our deacons will surely stop you, as you are not a member, you see. Besides, we don't believe in women singing anyhow."

"Then I'll have to listen to the men sing."

"Well . . . , not many do. Only those who are certain they belong to the predestined and take communion. Our deacons would like to forbid singing in the church altogether. But some of our Elders object. Now we sing only after the service, so that those who object can leave."

"And many do leave?"

"Certainly."

The verses chosen for singing were always from the Book of Psalms in the Old Testament. The rendition into awkward

English made singing them almost impossible, even by those with good voices, which were wasted harmonizing lines such as those of the 137th Psalm:

The rivers of Babylon
There when we did sit down
Yea even when we mourned when we left Zion
Our harp we did hang it upon the willow tree
Because there they that us away led in captivity
Required of us a song, thus asked mirth of us whose
      land was laid waste
Sing us a song then they said.

The Psalms were so crudely translated, they were almost impossible to sing:

And the earth did shake and quake
And stirred be
Grounds to the mount and shook for wroth was He.

Much later, when the Pilgrims who emigrated to America borrowed from the Bay Psalm Book of the Massachusetts Puritans, they would still have trouble giving a harmonious rendition to these Psalms.

Mrs. Brewster merely shrugged over the problem of singing Psalms, and lingered with the others in the entrance hall to greet their Scrooby friends. Once inside the church, it was gloomy. True, the sun shone through the beautiful stained-glass windows, but it was a pale sun which failed to reach the dark pews. The unused organ had been covered with a gray cloth since 1582, when the Puritans rented this ancient church and restrained the instrument from thundering forth its harmony into the vaulted space. An attendant brought each of the women a little wooden box, inside of which was an earthen bowl of burning peat to keep their feet warm in the chill of a late September Day.

The visitors remained for the entire four hours of the service, and even for the "deaconing out" of the Psalms after the meeting. A deacon mounted a rostrum, found the pitch by banging his brass tobacco pipe, and sang the first line. Those men of the congregation who felt assured they lived in full atonement imitated his words and tune as best they could. Then the deacon sang the second line and they followed.

It was a quiet group that returned to its quarters subdued by four hours of religious service. Hardly had they reached the street when suddenly every church bell in town began to peal, one taking it up from the other. From all directions men came running, carrying leather pails. Stir and bustle filled the once empty Sunday streets.

"Brand! Brand!"

"What is all this fuss about on Sunday?" William Bradford asked. "What are they shouting?"

"Fire! A house is on fire. With many houses built of wood, it is apt to spread swiftly."

"I am going to help fight the fire," William Bradford called out to the others, darting after a group of men.

"On Sunday?" Mary Brewster questioned.

William didn't even hear her, for the urge to help sent him off, running as fast as he could. A burning smell penetrated the street as gray smoke drifted over the roofs of the houses. Some Dutch women carried household effects beyond danger. A rosy blaze appeared overhead, and a few sparks fell on the English group.

"That William!" Mrs. Brewster said. "Not able to speak Dutch, how can he find our home all by himself? How is he to ask his way about? He'll miss the two o'clock meeting or will have to go to church without food. That boy William!"

A little before the two o'clock meeting, William returned. "We got the best of the blaze under control rather quickly," he said. "Only two houses burned down. I was told by a Dutchman, who spoke English, that sometimes a fire will take an entire street. There is a law now against building houses of wood; but there are still so many old ones left."

William had just time enough to eat some of the meal, which had the great charm of novelty: mussels en casserole, followed by slices of bread with Leidse kaas—cumin cheese. Then to church all of them went once more, this time followed by two women servants carrying hot footstools for the ladies. To add to their comfort, their hostess provided them with a lodderyn, a little bottle with l'eau de la reine, to pass to each other during the sermon.

After church and dinner, the family gathered in the living room for a glass of wine. The candles in the brass chandelier glowed, the hearthfire cheerily blazed. Looking into the burning, silvery birchwood logs, William Brewster said casually, "A canal boat will take us to Amsterdam this Tuesday morning."

His wife's eyes widened with surprise, "Why, William Brewster! Since when have you known about this?"

"Since this morning, but I couldn't discuss such matters until after sundown, could I? We'll need two pulled barges. There will be quite a crowd of us, you know."

The next day, a number of other Separatists arrived, bringing with them baggage which had come from Hull in England. Mrs. Brewster returned regretfully the borrowed Burgundian velvet cloak she had learned to like so much. "I ought to dress like all of the other Separatist women," she said. "Velvet and satin might blow out the fire of our wonderful Christian fellowship."

"Blow out the fire of what? How . . ."

"Speaking of a fire," Catherine Carver interrupted hastily, "may I go into the kitchen to learn from your cook how to bake those tasty smoked eel rolls you served this noon?"

"Of course! Of course!"

Catherine went quickly out of the room, but the cook's

conversation, alas, turned from smoked eel to the English girls.

"Such lovely girls! One of these days some Dutch boy will surely ask permission to marry one of them."

A Dutch boy marrying one of their daughters? It had never occurred to Catherine Carver that marriage would come to their children among the Dutch people.

"My husband," said Catherine Carver, "would know how to tell the young man off, but I wouldn't trust Mr. Brewster to decide. It worries me."

"If it worries you, then why don't you have the English girl engaged the Dutch way, if they are able to be married. It is quite simple, you know. If a young man likes a girl, he calls one evening in his best clothes. He is given a welcome without referring in any way to the reason of his visit. When candle time comes, you and your husband retire, leaving her at the fireside alone with the suitor. The two chat for a while, but the boy makes no proposal. If she lets the fire go down, it is a sign she won't have him for her fiance. But if she places a large log on the fire, it is a token she favors him."

"Why! It sounds scandalous! We wouldn't allow any of our young girls to be alone with a man for a minute. Not for a minute! Imagine! Dutch girls don't seem to be kept very strictly. I see."

"Not kept very strictly! In our country, if a woman ever shows any interest in a married man, she'll get the wooden petticoat."

"The what?"

"Two gendarmes put her in a wooden petticoat, which rests on her shoulders, with her head peeping out at the top and her feet left free, and they lead her about town."

"My! My! Yet, as far as I can see, Dutch women do seem more independent than we English."

"Yes, we always have felt we were independent, because within the walls of our homes, the wife manages. Not outside, of course. We would never correct our husbands in public. At home, though, I tell him not to use his napkin as a handkerchief, but to wipe his fingers on it. He doesn't listen much, but I keep giving him a napkin, even if he thinks it is a crazy, newfangled idea. Now, about your girls . . ."

Catherine Carver sped out of the kitchen, saying, "Oh, I forgot, I promised to arrange those fresh flowers."

She would always remember with appreciation the genuine friendliness and hospitality of the Dutch family whose home she shared for such a brief interlude.

Chapter 4

LEAVING MIDDELBURG BY BARGE

The day of departure from Middelburg arrived, luminous with the mellow glow of autumn. The sun's golden hue sparkled on the cobblestones as the Separatists walked to the barges hired to take them to their destination of Amsterdam. The sudden sound of the horn blown by the jager, driver of the towing horse, to signify the boat's departure, sent the sea gulls fluttering high into the air. And now the English group took their leave of the little wooden houses built helter-skelter along the canal. The first boat steered away from the quay, closely followed by the second; the sturdy horses pulled with all their might beside the canal. The boats moved slowly as the city gradually receded behind the travelers. They strained their ears to catch the last sounds of Middelburg, their temporary home. The loud cry of a woman mussel-seller reached them: "Two stuivers een emmer—twopence a pailful!"

The canal lay several feet higher than the surrounding farm land and, as William Bradford leaned over and scooped up a bit of the water in his cupped hand, he tasted it and exclaimed, "It's sea water!" Sea water above land level was indeed strange. He observed that most of the country was made up of little dry lakes that had to be reclaimed from the sea every morning by windmills pumping water out of the ditches into the canal. The ingenious Dutch had put to good use the wind sweeping down from the North Sea. Grain mills, wood mills, the green and white water mills went industriously about their task.

103

As William watched from the deck of the low-lying barge, he realized the indissoluble connection with the sea of his newly adopted country. Holland fought a never-ending battle for the possession of its land. Which would finally hold it, keep it, master it, the Dutchmen or the sea?

Before the year 1000, Holland was comprised of a number of small islands with 40 per cent of the area water, until a group of Dutchmen decided that, although God had indeed created the world, the Dutch would make Holland. They built a dyke around a tract of marsh and morass, which they drained of all salt water. They added another and still another bit of swamp, and connected each one with an island. One by one they cultivated these lots into fertile land and built farm houses on them. It was risky, for the sea ever sought to reclaim its own, as one dyke after another collapsed. But the Dutch, with volharding, perseverance, repaired each broken dyke and built new dykes which strongly endured.

To cope with the problem of sea water seeping in, the peasants dug a network of ditches and ladled the water out of each one with buckets into a canal whence it emptied into the sea. Such hand-by-hand work was much too slow a process for one enterprising Dutchman, who attached a couple of buckets to a wheel, and thus innovated a hand-worked mill. But could they keep the land from becoming water-logged when even this proved insufficient, as sea water kept seeping in?

Finally, in the 15th century, an unknown farmer contrived to put the omnipresent wind to good use, developing the windmill. Before long a great number of them dotted the landscape, and the soil was then kept dry and free of salt water. For centuries these mills needed no technical improvement, until the advent of steam and electricity replaced them as a source of power, but even today some of the old-fashioned Dutch windmills are still in use.

From their gliding barge, the travelers watched the ever-changing view. Here a sea gull flying up from the water, a little silvery fish quivering in its beak. Over there, ships and more ships passed by. That afternoon, the open sea arm of the harbor of Veere lay before them, where many ships with tall masts brought in riches from far-away lands. They could see the ropes coiled on deck, and here and there a cook looking out of his galley! Their eyes could hardly take it all in. There were dock workers, too, with flecks of wool on their clothes and faces. It was, indeed, a busy harbor scene. A seaman with a saucy monkey perched on his shoulders, dressed in a little black velvet suit trimmed with red satin and a round, flat beaver hat with a leather chin strap. A captain shouted orders to his crew. Four seamen played cards on deck. How their dark skins contrasted with the blondness of the Dutch! How many languages were being spoken—English, Dutch, Flemish, French, Swedish.

William Brewster's eyes kept returning to a man with a wooden peg that reached to his right knee, who was playing a nostalgic tune on his fiddle. It reminded him so much of his home in England and the harbor scenes of Hull and London that he impulsively tossed the player a couple of pennies.

"Do you smell the salt water?" John Robinson asked him.

"Yes, and the tar of the boats, too. Ah! What a good smell it is, of the high seas and far places, of youth and adventure!"

"It is the smell of our new country, William. It fills my heart to bursting."

William Brewster stared at John Robinson, grudgingly admiring his facility with words. William Brewster's hopes for a good life in this new country were also uppermost in his mind, and in the fullness of his soul, and in the tingling fibres of his body—hopes for adventure and a life of freedom of conscience on another continent. The mood was almost overwhelming.

He watched some little boys diving naked into the canal and took the opportunity to divert his companion from their growing sentimentality.

"In England swimming in public places is forbidden by law," remarked William Brewster.

As William had hoped, John was willing to change the topic. "Look at all those homes built in a row along that small canal," he remarked. "Each has its own drawbridge leading to a green painted door with an iron latch."

"The wind feels good on my face," William said gently to make up for his harshness to the younger man.

The wind made John Robinson's spirit soar and his face glow. His lips curved into a slow smile. "I'll never leave this country," he said with fervor; and he never would. Remaining behind as the faithful Pastor in Leyden, he encouraged the Pilgrims with the strength of his spirit and with his inspiring letters to Plymouth, Massachusetts, to those who settled there in the New England wilderness. He survived only until 1625, establishing a name and a reputation never to be forgotten in Pilgrim annals.

John Robinson, however, could not have foreseen his future then, as the towing horse pulled their barge to its berth at the quay of Veere. The crewmen roped the barge to a pile. Ringing a bell, the Captain let his voice go forth strong and clear: "There'll be a wait here of four hours! From one sluice gate to another down to sea level in ten feet! Our barge won't be able to sail until high tide brings the sea up a bit. Be of good cheer. Veere is having its annual fair. Please go to see it! All of you! Enjoy yourselves!"

"A fair! A fair!" the young girls and boys twittered as if they were so many birds. "Do you think as Christians we could go to the fair?" Mrs. Brewster asked Pastor Robinson.

To his own surprise, Pastor Robinson heard himself capitulating to the merry mood of the moment. "Everybody seems to be going, judging from the crowds on the street. We might as well join them. We have plenty of time and this is a new country, so let us see for ourselves what a Dutch fair is like."

Mrs. Robinson was still doubtful about whether it was Christian to go, but the Captain saved her from the awkwardness of the situation. "You ought to try our poffertjes, pop-overs," he said. "They are the specialties of a Dutch fair. Quite different from those in any other country."

It was indeed tempting to go to a Dutch fair even though it represented worldly pleasure. As Mrs. Robinson averted her eyes, she observed a new sight—two men, heavily draped in black, with black veils flowing from their tall hats, mournfully moving from door to door. It was evident from the distress of their listeners that they brought dismaying news.

"Look at those two strangely dressed men!" Mrs. Robinson said to the Captain, leaving unspoken a comment on her husband's decision of going to the fair. "What, pray, are they doing?"

A gleam of mischief was in the Captain's eyes as he explained the situation to Mrs. Robinson. "Oh, those are the *aanspreker en de huilebalk*—the undertaker's man and the official weeper. The undertaker's man is announcing to relatives and friends the death of a young girl. At the completion of his delivery of the message, the weeper will begin to cry."

Mrs. Robinson's hands moved to her face in sudden fear, putting her fingers over her eyes to shut out the unwelcome sight. "How do you know that they are announcing the death of a girl?"

"Simple . . . by the white rosette on their hats."

She thought dismally of her own little daughter and the very real dangers which awaited them in a strange country. The thought mellowed her mood, and in a voice tender with love for husband and children, she said, "We, too, are strangers here now in this country, and it behooves us not to be too stiff-necked. Come, let us go to the fair!"

Preparations started at once. Each traveler would carry a lantern to be lit when darkness fell. It was no small task to reach the site of the fair through the narrow streets, passing carts laden with herring barrels, and patrician gentlemen in velvet and satin on horseback, each followed by a page boy. Near the fair itself the streets became barely passable, yet women paused in curiosity before the little shops.

At the entrance to the fair, they were preceded by a butcher who proudly led a sleek, fat ox, his broad neck bedecked with gay garlands. A procession of weavers carried looms, which were also hung with flowers. Once inside the fair gates, the English group mingled with citizens in festive attire who thronged about the various games. There was a tempting array of booths laden with white lace caps and beautiful belts with silver clasps. Vendors offered candy in the shape of little windmills and farm animals. There were pieces of chocolate, that wonderful rich flavor the Spaniards had learned about in Mexico and whose use had spread to France and Holland as early as 1517.

At a fish stand, a man in native costume cajoled them into sampling pieces of his pickled herring. A gaily decorated stall featured a new invention, the iron cooking stove, about which women crowded to examine the flat iron pan indented with deep circles for the making of poffertjes. The popovers and waffles, served piping hot with butter and sugar melting together, were deliciously accompanied by large cups of hot anise-flavored milk.

Swings built for two, shaped like little boats, were painted bright red. The children ran straight to them. As they swung in the air, they shouted down to their parents to follow their example. To their utter delight, Pastor Robinson and William Brewster placed themselves in the swings and were soon flying up and away. Having tarried for a little chat in her broken Dutch with the wife of the owner of the waffle stall, Mrs. Robinson uttered a cry of surprise when she saw her erstwhile dignified husband and William Brewster sailing blithely through the air. From the swings to a jolly whirl in a nearby carousel was a small step this happy afternoon, as even Mrs. Robinson allowed herself to mount a painted wooden horse sidesaddle.

As she revolved, her full skirts billowed and her black bonnet fell backwards revealing her curls, which danced youthfully to the music as the boys and girls laughed with happiness.

The fascinating and fragrant gingerbread stall featured a huge flat cake displayed tantalizingly on a large chopping board with a meat cleaver at its side.

"Come, try your luck in chopping off a piece!" the vendor called out. "Two pennies for a cut!"

Each in turn tried his luck and to the surprise of everyone, young William Bradford won the largest piece. The afternoon was now far spent, and as dusk fell, they lighted their lanterns for the walk back to their two waiting barges. The sounds of the fair drifted to them in the darkness—vendors offering their wares, stray dogs barking. Tired from their many new impressions, all their activity and the gaiety, they reached their places of rest on the barges.

By dawn, the barges had descended through the sluices of the canal into the wide open sea arm, to the deep murmur of falling rain on the deck, which drew a veil over the water and grayed the coming light of a new day. By afternoon the rain stopped, and the passengers gladly left their cramped cabins to go up on deck.

"Look at those high dikes," the Captain said to a group of them. "Dikes, dikes everywhere! Our work here is never done. We are forever building or repairing dikes against the sea, which constantly rolls around us to threaten our very existence. Our fathers took the land from the sea and now our sons have to continue to hold it. Just a little crevice in a dike or a few hours of inattention and we would be faced by a devastating flood. Our farmers cannot even go to bed at night and be assured that in the morning their land will still be safely dry before their eyes, as they might very likely find it covered by the sea."

Warming to his theme, he continued reflectively, "That constant struggle for existence has not only bound us closer, but has made us ever alert both mentally and physically, because we can't afford to be selfish. We must bend our personal inclinations to the common good. What could one man on his own do on a dike?"

The Captain, like all men of the sea, served this demanding mistress with dedication. "Look at the sea," he said meditatively to those around him. "Look at these waters! It was indeed here that we succeeded in securing our freedom. If these waters could only talk, what a tale they would tell of our passion for liberty. For forty years we fought off Spain's domination and, just imagine, we secured our independence just recently. How historic!"

Although he was familiar with Dutch history even up to the present, having served as Secretary to Ambassador Davison when he was fresh out of college, William Brewster urged, "Tell us about it, Captain, tell us about your country's struggle for religious and political freedom."

"Well, an interesting story it is and since you will live in this land, it may prove worthwhile. All of you had better gather in the main salon and I'll give orders to my first officer to steer the barge in my place."

When the travelers were seated in the barge's one large public room, the Captain came in directly and began his discourse.

"As you all know, Holland has become a Protestant country. You Englishmen have sacrificed for your faith, but so have we. The Reformation of Martin Luther and John Calvin is an old story here. Let me tell you something of the sovereigns who have ruled over us, so you may better understand our situation. The past century has been one of great historic interest, not only to the Dutch, but to the many nations whose histories are interwoven with ours. After Christopher Columbus returned from his first voyage of discovery to America, Philip the Fair, who was born in 1473 and died in 1506, married Joanna, the daughter of King Ferdinand of Aragon and Queen

Isabella of Castile. Their son Charles, who was born in Ghent in 1500, became King of Spain through his mother, and Duke of Burgundy and the Low Countries through his father, and also Emperor of the Holy Roman Empire upon the death of his paternal grandfather, Maximilian.

"Charles V, who was carefully reared and educated, spoke many languages: Dutch, German, French, Spanish and Italian. In an appealing way, he could assume the milieu of each country he governed, democratic in his deportment with us, stately with the Spanish, witty with the Italians, vibrant with the French. He knew men and how to use them, employing the native born as his officials, because the haughty Spanish would be incompatible with our democratic ways. His mundane power was enormous. He liked to say that the sun never set on his domain, which was practically true, for he was at the same time King of Sardinia and Genoa, of the Duchy of Milan, of Spain and her immense colonies in America and in the Caribbean, and he was also declared Emperor of Germany.

"Naturally he had enemies, and his great rival was Francis I, King of France. The French were greatly weakened when they lost Tournai, which was passed to Belgium in 1521, and when they also lost the Battle of Pavia, Italy, in 1525. This was a disaster for France, since their sovereign, Francis I, was taken a prisoner by the enemy. It was during the reign of Charles V that the seventeen Belgian and Dutch provinces were grouped together under the name of Pays-Bas, or Netherlands.

"The South was composed of ten provinces: Limburg, Luxembourg, Brabant, Flanders, Namur, Hainault, Antwerp, Malines, Franche-Comte and Artois. The North comprised seven provinces: Zeeland, Holland, Utrecht, Gelderland, Over-Yssel, Friesland and Groningen. The word Netherland in the singular referred only to the province of Holland. When Pays-Bas was incorporated into the Empire of Charles V in 1548, as part of his realm of Burgundy, the Low Countries had a population of three million people. It was Charles V who brought together under one ruler what eventually became the Republic of the Seven United Netherlands."

The well-informed Captain pointed out that Charles V, as a good sovereign, continued the efforts of his Burgundian predecessor to centralize territories. Thus he worked to integrate all of the Low Countries' provinces and forced Francis I of France to relinquish his fiefs, feudal estates, of Flanders and Artois.

"Yes, we are indebted to Charles V because, although the Low Countries were theoretically a part of the Empire, still he persuaded the Diet of Augsburg in 1548 to free them from direct Spanish imperial jurisdiction. As a matter of fact from then on the region which was to comprise Belgium, Luxembourg and the Netherlands, for all practical purposes became a single state.

"Charles V maintained his court at Ghent, Brussels or Mechelen," the Captain continued, "which are in the South, and never at The Hague, Amsterdam or Utrecht, so that the French language and manners prevailed over those of the Dutch. Even those who were sent to rule in the North had little in common with the Dutch burghers, and so the Dutch took a dim view of their French overseers as foreigners.

"Essentially Charles V was a militarist, a man of action with a phlegmatic temperament. In spite of a certain personal charm and learning, he was still without any real sentiment. His goal was to retain his vast regal power. Therefore he demanded strict obedience to the crown, his hand ever ready to crush out any movement for reform. He punished as heretics any who refused to accept the dogma that the wafer and wine offered in the Catholic ritual of Holy Communion was actually the flesh and blood of Jesus Christ. Still, to be fair, it cannot be said that Charles V was ever a champion of the infallibility of the Roman Catholic Church, with which he himself was at variance in many instances.

"For such an intelligent ruler, Emperor Charles V made two glaring mistakes: he practised tyranny and he ate too much. Because of his unbearable tyranny, he was forced by his rebellious subjects to abdicate. At the rather early age of 55, his popularity was gone, his great fortune almost dissipated, his personal and commercial affairs in utter confusion. Gluttony finally ruined his health. His appetite was never appeased, as if he were constantly feeding an inner nervousness. Breakfasting at five on fowl, he would return to bed, then breakfast again when he awoke at nine, on meat delicately prepared with sugar and wine. For his mid-day meal, he consumed some twenty dishes. In the afternoon, he took some pastries and beverages to tide him over until the next meal, at eight in the evening, when he enjoyed a royal feast with his family and courtiers.

"The conclusion of his reign came towards the end of 1555 when Charles V abdicated at Brussels in favor of his son Philip II. It was a touching performance. The ailing father leaned heavily on the shoulder of his counsellor, the young German-born Willem, Prince of Orange, and with great eloquence and poignancy addressed the delegates who had assembled before him from all of the Low Countries. He was now laying down the burdens of his sovereignty of the vast empire in favor of his son Philip. He asked the listeners for respect and devotion in return for his own proven loyalty to the Empire. The delegates were so impressed they were almost moved to tears. Their mood changed quickly, however, when the King's son rose to speak.

"It was a meager beginning for the young man. Reared in Spain, Philip had never been able to master fluency in Dutch or in French, so he spoke to them in Spanish. But the foreign tongue was not the chief barrier. It was a certain lack of warmth, detachment over and above an excusable nervousness, a haughtiness of the high-born Spaniard. The reign of Philip II was to last for only four years, when he left for his native Spain, never to return. It was indeed ironic that he was driven out of the Netherlands by that selfsame Willem of Orange on whose shoulder his aging father had leaned during the abdication ceremonies in Brussels.

"Charles V was deeply involved in the Religious Wars. He had marched his armies against the armies of the Reformers and defeated them at Muhlberg in April of 1547, but he was unsuccessful thereafter and was forced to sign the Peace of Augsberg in Bavaria in 1555 between the Catholics and the Lutherans. His abdication followed, and his withdrawal to the Monastery of St. Just in the old Province of Estremadura in Spain, where, after having devoted a greater part of his life in opposing the Protestants, he died in 1558.

"Let me tell you a little bit about Charles' son and heir, Philip II, who became Emperor at 28 years of age. And indeed it was a great Empire. He was King of Spain and Sicily, titular King of England, France and Jerusalem, Absolute Dominator in Asia, Africa and America, and Hereditary Sovereign of the Netherlands. He held the destiny of the world in his hands. Born in Spain, he had married his cousin Maria of Portugal at 16 and a year later became the father of Don Carlos and a widower when his young wife died.

"Philip was never popular among the Dutch and he could not understand why we insisted on religious freedom. In his eyes, the Dutch were his subjects, but his feudal tyranny was like poison. The Dutch, as you know, take pride in their guilds which have great power, but he opposed them. Philip would not tolerate Protestantism and would not allow any Reformers to persist in his dominions, because freedom of religion leads to independence in government and the possible loss of these rich provinces of the Netherlands, which provided a major part of his royal income.

"While his father Charles V was still on the throne, he came as Prince to our country to exchange oaths of mutual fidelity, and from the beginning he did not seem to be happy with us. In our southern provinces of Flanders, the gay energy of the people annoyed him in contrast with the languid life in Spain. In the North, the loquacity of our burghers was a reproach to his own lack of repartee. Here, where education is stressed, our people speak many languages, whereas Philip spoke only Spanish. The year before his father abdicated in his favor, he had married Queen Mary Tudor of England in a political alliance. She was a tyrannical bigot, who had forbidden prayers to be said for the soul of her father, Henry VIII. Philip was silent, Mary talkative, and although small in stature she had a deep, masculine voice. Philip, too, was slightly built and had the heavy, hanging lips of Burgundian royalty and a protruding jaw, but a smooth and fair complexion and the blond hair of a Fleming. His bearing, however, was of a lofty royal Spaniard. Both agreed on the importance of maintaining the supremacy of the Catholic Church, but Mary was not devout and Philip was. However, his devoutness did not prevent him from being licentious. He would go about at night in disguise to visit the vice haunts, and when it was clear that his wife Mary Tudor could not bear a child, he left the country of England never to return—without regrets.

"Religious controversy was very early in evidence in our country," continued the Captain, who enjoyed the group's attentiveness to his unusual role of lecturer. "You see, the individualism of the Dutch people made them critical of clerical abuses in the Catholic Church. Many church offices were held by secular appointees, and some of their behavior was shocking to the clergy and dismaying to the pious. As early as 1375 a group was formed known as the Brethren of the Common Life. It was led by a man called Geert Groote, who had studied in Paris and believed in the power of humility. His movement spread through the Low Countries and into Germany. It stirred a religious revival which led to reform of practices in the monasteries. A monk who was named Thomas à Kempis, and who lived near Zwolle in the Province of Gelderland, is said to have been influenced by the writings of Geert Groote and his brethren, as evidenced in his book *Imitatio Christi.*

"You all know of Desiderius Erasmus. He was born in Rotterdam in 1467, was early trained by the Brethren, and became the Prince of the Humanists. Tutored by the Brethren, he disdained the subtleties of dogma with which Martin Luther justified his indictment of the Church. Erasmus stood on middle ground in regard to Luther, but when Pope Leo X condemned Luther as a heretic in 1520, Erasmus was not entirely against it, as he perceived in Luther the dangerous seeds of fratricidal conflict.

"I might add that Charles V, who had himself discoursed with Erasmus, and agreed with his ideas to reform the abuses of the Church from within, proved himself an apt opportunist, for when a papal delegate came to Antwerp to seek the King's support against Luther, he, in turn, sought the Pope's assistance against his enemy, France. Thus moved by political advantages, the Pope signed an edict ordering the destruction of Luther's writings throughout the Empire. Books began to be burned publicly at Louvain in 1520, and the first inquisitor was appointed in 1522 to destroy the Reformation.

"It was during the reigns of Charles V and his son Philip II that Martin Luther and Jean Calvin appeared, with the fearful consequences of the Reformation in their wake. Martin Luther, the son of a miner, was born in Eisleben, Saxony, in 1483, and died there in 1546. Jean or John Calvin, the son of a French cooper, was born at Noyon in Picardy and died in Geneva in 1564, where he was known as the Pope of Geneva. The forces set in motion by these men was beyond reckoning. It became a revolution which shook the world.

"In England you have your Puritans, and you who have seceded from the Church of England are Separatists. In this country we call them Reformers. They appeared at the time of Emperor Charles V, who justly believed in the primary importance of sustaining his imperial house, and he despised the Reformers as revolutionaries who threatened his omnipotence. Papal Rome required him to initiate the Inquisition, whose diabolical purpose was to annihilate every Protestant in our country.

"In Church history, the Inquisition was a court or tribunal for the examination and punishment of a heretic, nonconformists, dissenters, but in theology as actual or former members of a church, or those whose allegiance is claimed by it, who hold religious opinions contrary to the fundamental doctrines and tenets of that church.

"In 1559 Philip II turned the government of the seventeen provinces of the Netherlands over to his sister, Margaret, the Duchess of Parma, who formed a Council of State to assist her, comprising William, Prince of Orange, Count Egmont, Count Hoorn and others; then Philip returned to his native Spain. He instructed William to have a number of prominent citizens in the provinces of Holland and Zeeland arrested and brought before the Inquisition. William secretly had the victims warned in advance, and they were able to flee for their lives. Hundreds and thousands fled the country.

"Exasperated by the Inquisition, mobs in 1566 destroyed the images in churches and monasteries, burning and pillaging. From Spain, Philip answered these disasters by sending his representative, Ferdinand Alvarez of Toledo, the Duke of Alva, with an army of 10,000 men to restore law and order by punishing the Protestants who had been implicated in the disorders. The effect was electrifying, as 100,000 Protestants fled to the North. The Duke established a court which the people called the Blood Council, as it condemned to death those apprehended who had participated in the rebellion. It was this court, indeed, which found Counts Egmont and Hoorn guilty of high treason. These members of Margaret's governing body were beheaded in the Public Square in Brussels in June of 1568. The Duke ordered the arrest and condemnation of several hundred persons, and built a threatening citadel at Antwerp as headquarters of his army. With these measures, he subdued the provinces and introduced a system of taxing the people for the benefit of Spain.

"Meanwhile as matters reached a climax, William, who had professed Protestantism, left for Germany, where he raised an army in defense of his adopted country of the Netherlands. The Iron Duke's forces negated two attempts made by William to invade with his troops from Germany, and beat down all resistance.

"The Vatican upheld its part in the general madness. On February 16, 1568, it briefly announced that all heretics or Reformers were to be condemned to death. This meant men, women and children who had withdrawn from the state Roman Catholic Church. Human beings do not willingly submit to mass murder. Indignation was widespread as wild bands of revolutionaries retaliated by robbing and burning monasteries.

"In great despair the Low Countries united to protect themselves from the Duke of Alva's brutal methods. City after city renounced allegiance to Spain during 1572 and 1573. The Duke's troops crushed and sacked Haarlem, Naarden, Zutphen, Alkmaar and Leyden. Leyden and other cities withstood long sieges. As the people were reduced to starvation, Protestants and Catholics joined hands and resources to resist the despicable Alva, who was soon recalled to Spain, where King Philip II ordered him to proclaim a general pardon.

"The struggle here did not cease," continued the Captain, "as the protest gradually became anti-Catholic as well as anti-Spanish, especially so after the massacre of the Huguenots or French Calvinists, with which you are all familiar. It was Catherine de Medici, the mother of Charles IX, King of France, and Regent during his minority, who was the perpetrator of this foul deed. Fearing the growing influence of the Huguenots at court, she conceived the idea of exterminating her opposition by having all those of this sect living in Paris and elsewhere in

France ruthlessly killed. She obtained the consent of her son, and the slaughter took place on August 24, 1572, when more than a thousand people were slain. But the governors of many provinces refused to execute the orders for the killing of innocents while many took advantage of the reigning confusion to kill their enemies, and thus Catholics, too, were assassinated.

"The Catholic Church saw no reason for bloodshed, and many bishops and priests protected the non-Catholics whenever they could shield them from harm. This St. Bartholomew's Day massacre engendered a civil war, which lasted until Henry IV, a Protestant, came to the throne of France in 1589, and issued the Edict of Nantes granting the Protestants the freedom of their religion.

"But let's get back to our own Dutch history. When King Philip II recalled the Duke of Alva as General in 1573, he sent in his place Don Luis Requesens, who was in favor of establishing peace. He reduced taxes, but the war continued nevertheless, and the siege of Leyden took place in 1574. The Spanish troops in Antwerp mutinied for lack of pay and food, and recklessly burned down the city. King Philip continued to inflict his terrors from his palace in Madrid, and against our will and wishes, he appointed his half-sister Margaret, the Duchess of Parma, as titular head of our country. Margaret was the eldest natural daughter of Emperor Charles V; her mother, to whom the King was not married, was a Van der Genst of Oudenarde. Margaret was reared as a princess in the house of Count Hoogstraaten, and at twelve years of age she was married to Alexander, the 27-year-old son of Lorenzo de Medici, the nuptials celebrated with great pomp at Naples. This marriage was short lived, for within a year, Alexander was assassinated by his kinsman Lorenzino de Medici. Later Margaret married Ottavio Farnese, the nephew of Pope Paul II, and this, too, was an unequal match, for she was 20 and her bridegroom was only twelve.

"When she became Regent here at 37, she bore herself proudly. She was energetic and rather masculine in appearance, with some leanings toward the principles of the Dutch people. This made her half-brother Philip even more determined to establish a Court of Inquisition in every town and city of our country, but their ensuing cruelties resulted in open revolt.

"In April, 1566, some 400 nobles from the various provinces of the Netherlands congregated in Brussels to present the Regent Margaret of Parma a petition which they had drawn up requesting that the Inquisition and the edicts against heresy be moderated and that the States-General be convened at regular times, adding that there was great danger of revolt if this were not done. About 200 marched to the Palace, unarmed, simply dressed, approaching solemnly four abreast. When Margaret appeared and indicated to her advisers that she would promise to give serious consideration to this petition, Count Berlaymont, one of her counselors, exclaimed in surprise: 'Is it possible that Your Highness can fear these beggars!' When this derisive remark reached the petitioners, they adopted the name Gueux, Beggars, which gradually became the designation of all those who opposed Philip's government. Soon the cry of *Vivent les Gueux* was heard not only in noble circles but also among the burghers generally.

"In true Dutch spirit, the taunt became a password. Beggars indeed! From then on, Reformers dressed in the traditional beggar's costume, dull gray cloak with a little wooden alms cup attached to the cap in the manner of mendicant monks. Determinedly, they held out for religious freedom even in the face of death. Before long the trees were hung with corpses as a grim warning. 'If there is no more land left on which to take a stand, we'll fight for our freedom on the waters beyond the dikes.' The waters on which we are now sailing swarmed with self-styled Sea-Beggars, who became a terror to King Philip and his Spanish soldiers.

"In the meantime, groups of Reformers met secretly in the woods for hagepreken, field-sermons, but soon they went more openly beyond the city walls for these religious services, thousands of people attending these meetings. One day after such a gathering, as a large crowd passed a Roman cathedral, one said to the other, 'We are so much in the majority now, why should we be driven in disgrace outside of the city walls to worship our Lord? Let us therefore clear the cathedral of all images and claim it for our own.' The mob stormed inside and removed the images to the street, ruthlessly reducing them to rubble. As their fury mounted, one church after another was seized, emptied of images and claimed as a Reformed Church. Scandalized, King Philip's revenge was swift. His soldiers simply tore down these newly-converted Reformed Churches as well as those they constructed, and used the wood for gibbets from which to hang Reformers."

As the barge Captain talked on, the light of day grayed and deepened to an indigo blue. A thin rain began to fall, cold and dismal. The voyagers shivered with apprehension, horror-stricken by the Captain's vivid account of intolerance and brutality inflicted upon people such as themselves, who merely wished freedom of conscience. They, too, had experienced suffering and had seen educated men condemned to death in England for their faith. Would they be strong enough to sacrifice as much for their faith as the Dutch previously had done?

The Captain continued his illuminating discourse with the vigor of conviction of those who know they have not suffered in vain but have achieved their objective.

"The customary greeting of one citizen to another, in the days when the people fought off the Duke of Alva's Spanish soldiers, was 'The King of Kings is our ally!' To this, one replied, 'In Him do we put our trust!' It was not easy for even a tyrant like the Iron Duke to cope with such indomitable spirits, and some of the exploits of the Dutch have become legendary. Every parent tells his children of how, in 1572, when the Duke ordered his son Don Frederico to encamp with his army of 30,000 men about the walls of the city of Haarlem, midwinter found the canals frozen over. The Spanish soldiers, unaccustomed to the northern climate, slipped and slid over the ice-covered surface. Suddenly they beheld a group of Reformers, fully armed, glide on skates beyond the city gates and tackle unsuspecting guards, who were helpless on the slippery footing. Thus a great many were killed and the rest scattered in panic. Not to be outdone, the Duke of Alva ordered 7,000 pairs of skates for his Spanish soldiers, but they could never become as skillful on ice as native-born Netherlanders.

"Let me tell you, too, about King Philip's only son, Don Carlos. His mother was the Princess Maria of Portugal, who died when the heir-apparent of our country was born in 1544. By the time the child grew to manhood, his cruel, crafty and ambitious character was firmly set. As an apple does not fall far from the tree, he was not unlike his father. Sometimes he had an hypnotic effect upon people, and strange stories are told about his excesses, his gluttony and dastardly behavior. As a student at the University of Alcala in Spain, he fell down a stone staircase and suffered a severe head wound, which may have injured his brain. His temper was ungovernable and he was completely undisciplined. When a page who slept outside of his chamber door once failed to answer the ringing of his bell, the Prince seized the hapless youth and would have thrown him from the window if not prevented in time. When a shoemaker fashioned a pair of boots for him that proved too snug, he had the boots chopped up, cooked and served in a stew to the horrified shoemaker.

"Prince Don Carlos detested the Duke of Alva, because he regarded the Netherlands as his own special domain as heir to his father Philip's empire. Once he attacked the Duke of Alva with a dagger, swearing to kill him for defrauding him of his domain, and both men struggled violently, rolling on the ground, until separated by the King himself.

"Don Carlos was certainly not a loving character. Not only did he hate the Duke of Alva, but he bore no love for his father. In fact, he despised the King with a blazing hatred. This, of course, did not endear him to the older man, who in turn heartily disliked his unseemly son. Fearing for his life, the unhappy Prince always carried two pistols in his belt, even slept with them under his pillow.

"One excess led to another with this young scoundrel, who learned how to indulge his passions from his gentlemen-in-waiting, spending his gold, giving away his medals and even his embroidered garments in payment to ladies of the night. Someone at court alleged he had a liaison with the Queen, who was his stepmother, but the truth of this was never proved. King Philip, however, was exasperated enough over the incorrigibility of Don Carlos to write two letters in this regard to Pope Pius V. He gave the charge of incestuous amour as grounds for the young man's arrest and imprisonment. These letters, buried in the archives of the Vatican, asked the Pope's counsel on how the King could properly punish his wife and his son. History says that the accused were made to imbibe poisoned broth, and that both expired grotesquely within a few hours of each other. Spanish history is replete with horrors.

"With the death of the heir apparent, the desire for independence and religious freedom led the Netherlands to delcare war against Spain, and so in the year 1579 the northern provinces united to form the Dutch Republic. A proclamation to the people declared that Philip was no longer King, and, Regent Margaret having returned to Italy, that Prince William of Nassau, Lord of Orange, was invited to assume leadership as Stadhouder or Governor. William became the father of our country, advocating freedom of worship, the right to choose one's own church leadership, and the liberty to read the Bible. He believed also in education, and approved the Constitution of 1579, which guaranteed freedom of the press, education and religion, and right of association, assembly and petition. All of these ideas were new then and had never been advanced or regarded in any other country. The ruling office of the House of Nassau, which dates back to the 11th century, was made hereditary.

"Up to the time we originated our Constitution, we had believed in Kratia, government by the Aristo, the best—aristocracy, rule by the best. It cannot be improved upon, but who were the best? Certainly not the nobles, the patricians, the socially exclusive, nor the most wealthy of the community. So we changed our conception and accepted Kratia by the Demos—democracy, rule by the people."

As the Captain paused, the listeners, appalled by the account, turned to each other. The men frowned. Had they heard right? Had the captain actually used the word *democracy*? That despicable word! How could he, who seemed so educated and well informed, make such a radical statement? It was blasphemy. Democracy meant something low in the rung of government. Crowning the Demos, the common man, was like crowning a pig. How could a common man become a ruler in the place of nobility? The Dutch had radical ideas, but as for themselves, they would prevent any of their church offices from falling into the hands of anyone of the common herd. The Netherlands might be far advanced, but surely the head of a common man was not fit to wear a crown, thought the English exiles. As Christians, they loved all persons, but this did not signify that in church one had to sit indiscriminately next to anyone at all. In the matter of choice of officers for the church, only an honorable So-and-so of Such-and-such of social standing was suited to become an elder or assume the chairmanship of any of their committees.

"King Philip of Spain came in person accompanied by 90 ships to force us back under his rule and into the Catholic Church," the Captain continued. "But within four years time he had to depart. When he sailed from the very harbor we have just left, a disillusioned man, a great storm overtook him and his ship sank. The monarch himself was rescued, but his rich clothing and jewels were lost. When he reached the coast of Spain, he knelt down upon the earth and bitterly vowed to devote the remainder of his life to the extermination of every

Protestant in the Netherlands. He soon found that to be an impossible task, for we had chosen the right leader in Prince William of Orange, who made the office hereditary, and a good decision that was too. If ever a country selected a superior house to rule, it was ours."

His listeners still attentive, the Captain continued to speak of Dutch history. "Let me tell you now a little about William of Orange, who was born in 1533. He was one of five sons of the Count of Nassau-Dillenburg. Upon the death of his father, William of Nassau, he inherited at the age of eleven several rich estates in Germany as well as the Netherlands, and succeeded to the principality of Orange in southern France. He was early trained in leadership. His mother reared him as a Lutheran, but he could take possession of his estates only if he would become a Roman Catholic, live in the Netherlands, and participate in the Burgundian Court at Brussels. He conformed to these requirements, became a page in the court of Emperor Charles V at Brussels, and at 18 was the trusted counselor and confidential friend of the Emperor. He listened well and was discreet in his speech so that the Dutch called him Willem de Zwijger, William the Taciturn, rather than the Silent.

"When he was 18, he married Anne of Egmont, daughter of Count Van Buren, the wealthiest noble of the country. At 20, as commander of an army, he was rich, powerful, and of sovereign rank, with a princely, luxurious life of banquets, masquerade balls, tournaments and military displays. At Brussels, he enjoyed the grandeur of the royal palace, attended by 24 noblemen and 18 pages. Royal hospitality sometimes required as many as 28 cooks in the vast kitchens.

"A born soldier, orator and diplomat, he was one of the most heroic and fascinating characters the world has ever known. When King Philip II, son of Emperor Charles V, sent the 29-year-old William of Orange to the Netherlands as his representative, little did he imagine the Prince would boldly declare himself independent of Spain.

"Above average in height, well-built, spare and sinewy with a somewhat severe face, brown hair and eyes, William combined his highly developed intellect with the practical qualities of a military man. Certainly not taciturn, although he kept silent in official conferences, preferring to listen, he was indeed affable and ready-witted, enjoying good conversation.

"Instead of the Silent, he could have been called Silvertongued, for he was an able debater and writer. Letters are extant addressed to King Philip and to the Regent Margaret, some forty pages in length, of good literary quality. He was fluent in Latin, French, German, Spanish and Dutch.

"When he converted to the Reformed Church, he turned devout, relying implicitly upon Divine guidance. He was tolerant, long in advance of his time, in extending freedom of worship to Catholics and to Anabaptists. He befriended Dutch Protestants and the Huguenots or Calvinists of France, who all can be classified as Reformers.

"William of Orange and his four brothers led our people against the powerful Duke of Alva. The Nassau family's losses were costly. William's three brothers lost their lives and the estates of the Prince were confiscated, yet he remained faithful to the revolt, furnishing us with new armies wherever most needed, as city after city hailed him as their savior. In a letter to King Philip, the Duke of Alva boasted, 'I'll not leave a single Protestant alive. If I fail in this siege, my wife, the Duchess, shall come from Spain to take my place.' But he was universally despised. Even his own son, Don Frederico, could no longer stomach his atrocities and openly opposed his father. When a deputation of Dutch matrons asked Don Frederico's protection for women in childbirth against the abuse of roving Spanish soldiers, he granted it. Homes with lace bows attached to the door knob, signifying confinement, were to be exempt from raids. Finally, when the Iron Duke's soldiers grew sick of the carnage and mutinied, Alva struck his tents and departed, leaving behind a name which lived on in infamy.

"This was not the end. The King of Spain sent a new fleet to the Netherlands with 15,000 soldiers under the command of Pedro de Melendez. Fortunately for the Dutch, the ships were still in the Bay of Biscay when a devastating plague killed half the men, including Don Pedro himself, so there was little else for King Philip to do but abandon his punitive enterprise. He decided it would be easier to have Prince William of Orange removed from the scene of action. Believing that William was the great obstacle to the reconquest of the Dutch provinces, Philip had offered a large sum of money, and also a part of William's property and a title of nobility, to anyone who would either capture or slay the leader of the Dutch provinces. With these inducements as an incentive, several unsuccessful attempts were made on the life of the Prince. But in July 1584, a young Burgundian, Balthazar, who avowed that his parents had been executed because of their religion, and who although Catholic pretended to be a Calvinist, spurred no less by religious fanaticism than by hope of the reward, managed to gain entrance to William's mansion in Delft.

"With the medal of the Order of the Beggars around his neck, the Prince and his elegantly attired company rose from the noon meal to retire to the upper rooms. As William ascended the stairway Balthazar emerged from its beautiful arch and, only two feet from the Prince, fired three bullets from his pistol into his chest. The victim, realizing his doom, exclaimed in French as he fell mortally wounded, 'Oh my God, have mercy upon my soul! Oh my God, have mercy upon this poor people!'

"As the murderer escaped through a side door and ran toward a rampart to jump into the moat surrounding the palace, he stumbled, fell, and was promptly seized by several pages and halberdiers. Beyond the moat a horse waited for his getaway. When told the Prince was dead, he was gratified by the accomplishment of his intent, but when subjected to torture to determine the plotters, he confessed it was the president of the Jesuit

College at Treves who had instigated him to the deed in behalf of King Philip, who had offered 25,000 crowns for the performance of the crime. When Balthazar was caught and executed by the Dutch, his parents received from Philip the three seignories of Lievremont, Hostal and Dampmartin in France as a reward. In addition they were ennobled and became part of the landed aristocracy.

"A great and beloved Dutch leader had fallen. Fifty-one years old at the time of his death, he left a wife and twelve children, whose personal sorrow was shared by the entire nation when he was entombed at Delft, between The Hague and Rotterdam.

"For almost two decades he had resisted the power of Philip II. As a soldier he had only fair success, but as a statesman and diplomatist he occupied a foremost place among his contemporaries. Moreover, in an age of religious fanaticism, he stood on the side of moderation, strongly disapproving of the iconoclasm of his coreligionists. Philip himself gave testimony to the importance of his doughty opponent as a leader when he placed such a high price on William's head. By the Dutch, William of Orange is gratefully remembered as 'Vader des Vaderlands.' "

The Captain, pleased at the marked attention of his audience, continued his narrative. "When Philip heard the news of William's death, he rejoiced, believing that the last obstacle to reconciliation between Spain and the Dutch Netherlands was removed. But Philip was miscalculating; William's place was taken by his second son, Prince Maurice, since his oldest son was a prisoner in Spain. King Philip hastily sent out his Armada for a quick conquest. The ships sailed proudly into the English Channel, where the wrath of the Sea-Beggars awaited them. Without warning, they attacked furiously with their hundreds of small boats, and were successful in sinking the Spanish fleet. They then sailed boldly on to Gibraltar, where they destroyed the rest of the Spanish navy in its own harbor. Nevertheless, it took Spain a long time to admit they were unable to conquer the Netherlands. Ultimately, unable to rule them, they had to allow religious freedom as well as Dutch independence."

The Captain, his eyes now gleaming with patriotic fervor, recounted with pride how the Dutch had proclaimed their independence, and how Spain had sent her envoy to The Hague for the signing of an armistice even before the Dutch reached the city of Amsterdam. "Right now the world is reading in great amazement our daring Declaration of Independence, thousands of copies of which have been printed and already distributed."

"Are they for sale?" William Brewster asked.

"Of course they are. Everywhere on our streets."

"Then I'll buy a copy the moment I arrive at Amsterdam. I'll keep it with me wherever I go," said Brewster.

"And read it aloud to those of us who can't read," said one of the Englishmen, "otherwise we could never get to know it."

"Oh, but you certainly will," the Captain said quickly, "because in this country we have a habit of turning any current event into a popular ditty. You will hear parts of our Declaration of Independence sung by the grocery delivery boy, just as you'll hear a number of other events dramatized in song by your butcher boy and by your milkman as they go about the streets."

"What are the events they sing about?" someone asked.

"Oh, mostly those typifying our struggle for freedom. They have become folk songs which appeal to our boys and girls more than any history lesson ever could. You'll hear them sung everywhere, songs like the sad ballad of Annette van der Koven, the beautiful Dutch girl who was tried for heresy and condemned to be buried alive. 'Forswear your faith and you'll go free!' a Catholic priest urged, but she refused. 'Return to the Catholic Church!' 'No!' she cried out bravely, and repeated her 'No' until her dying breath.

"There is another one about Herbert Willemse, the hardy,

faithful blacksmith of Naarden. The town had surrendered to the Spanish troops, and as they tried to enter his home, he snatched up a three-legged stool in one hand, a sword in the other, and stood in the doorway to defend his freedom. Overpowered by numbers, he sank to his knees, pulled out the two sharp swords the soldiers had plunged into his body, and in doing so severed the ends of some of his fingers. 'Return to the Catholic Church!' cried a priest, and for an answer he flung his fingertips into the cleric's face."

Finally, the discourse came to an end as the tantalizing smell of fried salmon drifted into the salon of the barge, and the travelers went to their tables. As the barge glided slowly along, they spent the rest of the day looking at the passing scenery. But the next morning Samuel Fuller, John and Bridget Robinson and young William Bradford conversed with the Captain as he steered the barge.

Somewhat suddenly, John Robinson asked the Captain, "When did Holland become a Christian country?"

"Comparatively late, I would say; somewhere between the years 500 and 800 A.D. From that period on, until 1482, the state of religion was rather disorganized," the Captain said; then continued reflectively, "We were, however, the first to supplant feudalism by democracy, and the first to prevent any prelate or prince from maintaining a superior position against our town governments. As you know, in England, King John signed the Magna Carta in 1215 at Runnymede at the demand of the barons and clergy. Here we originated the practice of town notables hearing from the people before reaching any decisions or making any laws, at a time when such was not practiced in any other nation."

The barge had now reached the old city of Dordrecht, about 30 miles from The Hague and 16 from Rotterdam. A team of dray horses came to tow it into the city through the Water Gate, on which was painted a large picture of a pretty milkmaid sitting on her stool and milking a contentedly chewing cow.

"Why the picture of a milkmaid?" William Bradford wanted to know, forever looking at things from his practical point of view.

"Oh, it is just one of the symbols of our battle for freedom. The young woman is honored because she performed a heroic deed for our country. About two years ago that milkmaid went to the meadow one morning to milk the cows and detected several thousand Spanish soldiers lying in ambush to take the city. She pretended to see nothing, quietly finished her milking, and returned to her bouwery or farm while singing a cheery song."

"Bouwery!" William repeated after the Captain, memorizing the Dutch word. "Once back on her bouwery, what did she do?"

"She ran into town to tell the burgomasters that she had seen the enemy soldiers. They swiftly ordered the opening of the sluices to let the sea come in, even though they knew the salt water would kill the crops and spoil the land for four years to follow. The Spanish soldiers fled before the onrushing waters in panic, and our city was saved. The farmers were reimbursed by the town for their lost crops, and the milkmaid was given an allowance for life, besides having her picture engraved on our guilders and stivers, as well as the Water Gate you have seen."

A number of the men and women listened attentively as the Captain retold the stories of Holland's struggle for freedom in behalf of human dignity.

"How brave you people are!" William Bradford said. "I would . . ." and his voice trailed off. He intended to say that he wanted to adopt their country for his own, which indeed he later did, although he was not to become a permanent resident. Just then he dared not express such an idea as forsaking his own native England. Yet the softened expression of his face plainly enough said that he had found a new country to his liking. A number of the others responded warmly to William's words, happy to have found a country of freedom of conscience. Before they had been in Holland long, some 30 of them applied for Dutch citizenship.

"We Dutch are a freedom-loving people all right," the Captain continued. "We don't want to be bullied by force of arms. Look to the east of you, across Kromme Zee—Curved Sea."

"Across Gramercy?" William Bradford asked, giving the name an English pronunciation so as to keep it in his mind forever.

"Not far from there lies the city of Breda, which is in the southernmost province of North Brabant, a bustling, cobblestoned city with a castle which was the favorite retreat of Prince William of Orange. It also fell to the Spaniards, but a year ago we recovered it. It happened in this way: A boatman promised to supply the Spanish garrison with peat, and one day, in sheer recklessness, he decided to take back the town. 'Stow away as many Dutch soldiers as my little boat will hold,' he told Prince Maurice. 'I'll cover them with peat and tow them right into the city.' Sixty-eight young soldiers volunteered for the task. When a Spanish corporal came on board from the citadel to inspect the cargo, he found nothing amiss, but under cover of midnight darkness our soldiers clambered on shore, did away with the sentinels, and retook the city."

Chapter 5

A BURIAL AT ROTTERDAM

To most Englishmen of the time, a Catholic was an idolator who strove to recapture North Europe for an Italian Pope. By the same token, in the eyes of a Catholic, a Reformer or Protestant was a revolutionist set upon willfully destroying a world-wide spiritual empire. And for what purpose? So that a greedy Protestant king might enrich himself with the long-held properties of the Church. Both parties were adamant in their beliefs, clashing their forces with great shedding of innocent blood.

As men and women of the 16th and 17th centuries, the Pilgrims stood for the real values of life and against the prevailing superficiality. Eternal verities and quality were the keynote in contrast to material riches. Discoveries of new worlds had brought quick wealth, many accumulating holdings in such far-away places as India or in America. Daring Dutch navigators, who sailed tall ships over the waters of the globe, had reached and taken Indonesia by way of the Cape of Good Hope. Profits from these lengthy voyages were enormous. Holland's leading statesman, Johan van Oldenbarneveld, fostered the merger of the several India companies in 1602 into the United East India Company, and within a short period it controlled the valuable Spice Islands of the Indies. As a result of this commerce, Holland built a great colonial empire.

The Dutch hoped to keep these Spice Islands to themselves. Since the sea route by way of the Cape was open to ships of other nations, the Dutch wanted to find a more direct route between Amsterdam and the East Indies by way of the Arctic, but success in this endeavor was to elude them. Of the five expeditions they launched, all were lost in the ice blocks of the Arctic Ocean. Yet they did not lose hope. The United East India Company had learned of Henry Hudson, an explorer who was a Captain in the service of the British Muscovy Company. They sent for him, found he was willing to assume great risks, and gave him a contract, a ship, crew, food and supplies in expectation of his finding a new way to the East Indies. His voyage on the Half Moon, Halve Maan, took place a little less than six months before the Puritans arrived in Holland from England.

The English exiles were to spend an interesting and challenging year in their next home in Amsterdam, before, as wanderers, they fared to their next home in Leyden, where they would find homes and employment for some ten years.

The distance covered from Middelburg to their destination in Amsterdam was marked by two distinct experiences for the English refugees: the unexpected discourse of the Captain of the barge, which greatly enlarged their knowledge of the country in which they would live for the next several years, and the realization that none of them could expect to escape the human condition no matter in which country they lived. They would know joys and sorrows and finally disappear from this world. Death itself was the final enemy, and death visited the barge on its otherwise serene voyage to bring tears and heartbreak to one of their women passengers, whose husband met with a fatal accident.

It happened suddenly. They saw a woman run to the staircase of the men's hold, waving her arms in panic. Several men passengers ran after her as fear snapped at their heels. At the top of the staircase, they came to a full stop. There lay a man crumpled in a heap at the bottom of the stairs, his back strangely bent and one leg doubled under him.

"He fell down the stairs a moment ago," Samuel Fuller said. "It was headlong. He is unconscious."

The victim's wife hurried to his side. Tears welled up in her eyes as she followed the men carrying him to his bunk. Another woman came forward to assist her and the two sat beside the narrow ledge of a bed. Most of the men returned to the deck and spoke little as they leaned on the railings, listening to the slap of the waves at the side of the barge, in a rhythmic chant of "death . . . death!"

The next morning, the window-tapper with his long bamboo pole was still going his rounds to awaken the citizens, when the boat reached Rotterdam, that ancient, strongly walled city, so well fortified, which had already become one of Europe's largest and richest harbors. The dawn was cold and clear; the water glittered like smooth ice in the first silvery rays of autumn, but the woman down in the men's hold, sitting disconsolately beside her husband's bunk, saw nothing of this early morning splendor. She knew that her husband was failing rapidly. Yet, she had noticed that when the barge stopped, no heavy-handed bailiffs nor soldiers came on board to search their belongings. It would seem that Holland was truly a country of freedom with friendly, warmhearted people.

During the night, as she had kept watch over her husband, a black abyss of despair opened before her. One by one her dreams sank into it, all her hopes and expectations of a new and better life in Holland. A number of women came in for the customary lamentations at the approach of death. Their loudly recited prayers showed great devotion, but brought little consolation.

Among those who came was Isaac Allerton and his wife Mary, who spent most of the night with her. The couple were not too popular, as Mary was considered too talkative and Isaac too ambitious. While in London he was a tailor; now, as treasurer entrusted with the communal purse of the group, his boldness had increased. Yet he kindheartedly helped Samuel Fuller bleed the patient and cut up blackweed and nightshade to be taken in a glass of beer every hour during the night. As was his wont, he argued a great deal with Samuel, who was their bleeder, physician and surgeon, to burn more and more brimstone and pimpernel as a fumigant for the cabin and a precaution against infection of the other passengers. He wanted to be sure the other men who were sleeping in the hold were well protected. It was Isaac who called the wife of the sick man with a gasp of despair when she dozed off for a moment, "Awake! Awake! Your husband collapsed the moment you dozed off! Now he is gone! Gone!"

The stricken woman spread her hands as if to hold the persistent flow of sorrow back. With the motion came the consciousness of what was expected of her as a grieving widow. She slumped to her knees beside the bunk and gave vent to an unearthly wailing. As if her cries had called them, Pastor Robinson and Elder Brewster came in quickly, followed by a number of women, who began at once to cry their hearts out in the well-accepted custom. It was their way of expressing their deep sympathy. The men of the hold had arisen and grouped themselves around their Pastor and Elder. Pastor Robinson stood in their midst, yet at the same time silent in solemn isolation. He felt for his pewter tobacco-box and his short pipe. Nobody looked surprised or irritated when he struck a flame with his tinderbox and lit his pipe, placed a cover of brass wire over the bowl, and began to smoke. One and all followed his motions. with approval. When he slowly removed with a pricker some obstruction from the tube of his pipe, nobody moved an eye.

Then he began to speak, deliberate at first, then with increasing emphasis. His words of consolation engulfed them like the waves of the sea, sweeping away every doubt of an eternal life of joy and peace awaiting all of them. He quoted the beautiful 23rd Psalm, so ancient, so appropriate, so truly comforting to the broken-hearted. "The Lord is my shepherd; I shall not want. He maketh me to lie down in green pastures; he leadeth me beside the still waters. He restoreth my soul. He leadeth me in the paths of righteousness for his name's sake. Yea, though I walk through the valley of the shadow of death, I will fear no evil for thou art with me, thy rod and thy staff, they comfort me. Thou preparest a table before me in the presence of my enemies. Thou anointest my head with oil; my cup runneth over. Surely goodness and mercy shall follow me all the days of my life and I will dwell in the house of the Lord forever."

Inasmuch as the towing-boat would stay all day at the quay, loading and unloading, it was decided to have the funeral services at Rotterdam. The widow sat in a circle of women friends in the salon, where the husband's body lay in state on a black-draped mourning bed, receiving the condolences of the Pilgrims. Friendly hands had secured the black mourning clothes required. Black veils trailing from their bonnets, some even to their feet, indicated the women's degree of mourning. Chairs, tables, mirrors and pictures were shrouded in black crepe. Callers were served wine with slices of bread and cold meats.

Since none of the English present were able to speak Dutch, the Captain hired local pallbearers for the funeral service. The Pilgrims, like the Dutch, observed the biblical custom of hiring mourners to weep, as mentioned in the Old Testament book of Ecclesiastes: "Man goes to his long home while the mourners go about the streets." In their eyes, this meant wearing black clothes, black gloves, and a black scarf draped from the crown of their hats. John Carver and Isaac Allerton, who were both past 30, were asked to wash the body of the deceased and dress it in fresh night clothes before he was laid out in state.

All the English, men, women and children, joined the funeral procession which left the canal boat that afternoon. In spite of their restrained manner, they loved drama and their souls feasted upon it. The hearse was drawn by four black horses whose backs were covered by black cloth, with black plumes on their heads. A train of black coaches followed, carrying the members of the deceased's family and close friends. Others attired in black walked slowly behind the coaches. There were no flowers; the Pilgrims did not use them at any of their services, including weddings. There was no religious ceremony; as Bible Christians they didn't believe in it. No words of esteem were spoken and there was no prayer said at the graveside, as this might be interpreted as praying for the soul of the departed. But they saw to it that the man was properly buried with his feet towards the East, "whither he must hasten at the sound of the last trumpet." Along the way to the burial place and especially at the graveside, the weeping of the bereaved was soul-satisfying. Then, when all was properly attended to, they enjoyed a hearty meal in a nearby tavern with new beer and old wine.

They had merely briefly experienced Rotterdam, which got its name from the River Rotte that empties into the Maas. As early as 1600 it was the second city of the Netherlands, lying some 13 miles southeast of The Hague and 48 miles from Amsterdam. It was destined to become, by our time, the most important harbor in the world. Rotterdam and Amsterdam, because of their strategic location on the North Sea at the mouth of Western Europe's largest rivers, made the Netherlands a stable and transit market. The financial transactions connected with this trade supported a large banking business.

Rotterdam sits astride the New Maas River and the main outlet of the Rhine. Its enormous inland harbor 15 miles east of the North Sea served as the main link between traffic on the Rhine to Central Europe and coastwise sailings to Norway, Denmark and Sweden, as well as to the Mediterranean and overseas. On its old cobblestoned streets walked some great personalities of history, like Desiderius Erasmus, scholar and theologian. As portrayed by the German artist, Hans Holbein, he was short and stocky, fair-complexioned, with blond hair and light blue, keenly intelligent eyes, intensely and humorously alive. His contemporary Hugo Grotius, Dutch jurist, theologian, historian, and of course William of Orange, called the Silent, were also to be seen in Rotterdam.

The next day, the wind, accompanied by a splashing rain, howled through the sails. Striding up and down the deck, William Bradford jerked his coat closer about him, not minding the rain, which he was used to. He watched the big warehouses of Rotterdam disappear one by one as the barge passed by. He was sorry to leave Rotterdam, unlike most of the others from England, to whom the hustle and bustle of the cities were repulsive, preferring their ancestral farms. William Bradford looked beyond farming to a larger life. He wanted above all to study, so when he met the Captain on deck, he abruptly asked, "Has Rotterdam any schools?"

"Has Rotterdam any schools?" the Captain repeated in disdain, as if the question had been asked in contempt of the Netherlands' educational progress. "We have them everywhere. We were the first to have schools supported by the state. Even England has none, so our country can rightly be called the intellectual capital of Europe, with its distinguished lawyers, physicians, painters and scholars. We treasure our philosophers, theologians, historians and mathematicians. You'll find that we owe our eminence not so much to the aristocracy as you in England do, but to the advancement of the average man. Our statesmen, scientists, writers, and painters are just burghers, the sons of merchants and manufacturers, and some of the men whom your King James still calls 'base mechanics.'

"A few months ago in a street of Breda a crowd gathered at a corner. What attracted them? It wasn't a street brawl, a cock fight or bull baiting, but a peculiar paper. Yes, a paper! And one with a mathematical problem on it at that! When a young French soldier passed by, he pushed through the crowd, to ask what it was all about. He learned that the problem had been submitted to the general public for solution. The young soldier was given a translation in both French and Latin. A few days later he sent in the correct answer, signing it simply 'Descartes.' The great mathematician was thus discovered by the common burghers on one of our main streets.''

As the barge moved on, William Bradford admired the gabled houses which lined the quay. There were staired gables, neck gables, bell gables and frame gables. Gables even ornamented the windows, the coat of arms and the steps. Some were decorated with gold leaf, others had masks of beautiful women for corbels. Colorful frescoes adorned many an upper building wall. As he looked at the passing scene, the sob of the wind echoed in the sails. William watched the clouds drift by as the rain stopped. Instinctively he took shelter from the cold in a doorway, and for a long time stood absently twisting his hat round and round his fingers, as he tried to plan a future for himself in Holland.

In the dreamy hour of dawn, the canal boat finally reached the quay of Leyden. As darkness had not completely lifted from the sleeping city, the oil in the street lamps still burned. Only William was up and about. He gazed at a solitary star, still piercing the copper green of the skies. The vessel, bathed by every little wave, splashed and plowed on its way toward the final destination—Amsterdam. William watched the water come in between the piles of the quay and flow out again. Here and there in deep holes boys were already fishing for the eels for which the city was famous. Looking at the freshness of Holland's landscape, a yearning crept into William's heart. Meadows that had never known any thirst and foliage that had gathered all the coolness of the flowing canals transferred their contentment to him.

Later in the morning a number of the men joined him on deck. Their unwillingness to admire nature for herself and a characteristically English feeling of superiority made them disdain any culture different from their own. Yet paradoxically the Bible, which was their guide and trust, was replete with the beauties of nature, its fullness and promise. There was fear in their hearts, for, as Bradford many years later remarked in his history, they saw "many goodlie and fortified cities and they heard ye strange and uncouth tongue and beheld ye different manners and customs and strange fashion of ye attires."

Nevertheless, that morning they could not help but admire the beautiful cultivated land their boat passed. The soil, saturated with moisture to an inky blackness of fertility, spoke of a good future of harvests. The rustling foliage, the shadows lying blue upon the fields, told them that the land had never known the dread of drought. There were well-cared-for farms, stately country homes, gaily dressed women tending their gardens, and red-cheeked, tanned farmers. The exiles hated city drudgery, wishing they could find work in the country. But they realized that if they became farmers, they would lose their religion, for the group would have to scatter for a livelihood in the outlying districts and could not come together for their church meetings. In the city, on the other hand, they would have to become twine-makers, wool-combers, or candle-makers. If they became full-fledged craftsmen, they would have to be Dutch citizens to join the powerful Dutch labor guilds. Pride of being English still glowed in their faces. Next to their religion, it was their proudest possession. They hoped they could find something better to do for their living than menial tasks. Not all of them could read and write well enough to teach English. In Holland, they were told they could write "Mr." before their names. This right was free to anyone, which was not true in England. But being called "Mister" would hardly secure one the income of a gentleman. Actually it was a minister in England who was called "Mister," abbreviated to "Mr.," because almost invariably he had taken the college degree of Master of Arts. The title "Reverend" was seldom if ever used for clergymen in England, or even in New England before the close of the 17th century.

The towing horse pulled the barge very close to a quay

where barrel hoisters and wagon loaders were briskly going in and out of a large brewery. Beer! Surely some of them could become brewers, or probably coopers, making and mending barrels. They watched as an itinerant trader took a pack off his back and opened it to display some rosettes for shoes to a woman standing in her doorway. No, they couldn't ever become vendors, as they lacked the money for the goods, and besides, they couldn't speak Dutch. But now the thoughts of the travelers turned to Amsterdam, their next home in the Netherlands.

Chapter 6

IN AMSTERDAM

There appeared on the horizon late that afternoon a city built around a dam at the mouth of the small river called the Amstel. First known as Amsteldam, its fame had spread so far and wide that some of the Pilgrims mistook it for an independent city-state. At that time the city authorities were in the process of building a series of concentric canals running through and around the city. It was a modern, progressive, innovation, the interior waterways proving far more economical for transportation than roads. The symmetrical rings of canals would ultimately be laced together by 400 bridges.

While Amsterdam was the nation's capital, the seat of the government was at The Hague, with its many magnificent 17th century houses. Amsterdam's history began in 1204 when Gieselbrecht III built a dam on the river, so the enclave was called Amstelredamme. A small fishing village, it came into the possession of the Counts of Holland by 1296, and by 1482 it was already a strongly walled city.

During the Middle Ages, Antwerp was the great rival of Amsterdam, but when the Spanish suppressed Antwerp, it declined, its Protestants and Jews driven out by the Inquisition. It had been Europe's greatest diamond center because of its location convenient for ships arriving from India, but after the Spanish conquest of 1576, many diamond experts fled north to Amsterdam. During the 17th century master gem-cutters from persecuted religious groups all over the continent continued to find refuge in Amsterdam. Along with the discovery of Brazilian diamond fields, this gave the diamond industry there a great lift. The closing of the Schelde River also precipitated immigration to the north by exiles from the ruined Flemish provinces. Many settled in Amsterdam because of its reputation for religious toleration and its respect for freedom of conscience.

Arranged in a semicircle with four main canals, Prinsen, Keizer, Heeren and Singel, and the dam in the center, the buildings rested on wooden piles driven from 14 to 60 feet through sand, mud and solid clay. These Dutch piles never rotted because the salt marsh petrified them. Amsterdam's most ancient building had been consecrated in 1306. This is the Old Church, Oude Kerk, dedicated to St. Nicholas; its 220-foot-high observation tower still offers a magnificent view of the ancient city of Amsterdam. A few stately patrician houses are extant today, owned by descendants of the merchant princes, who have not allowed them to fall into disrepair.

Early in the 17th century, the city appeared modern in many ways. It sustained a bank, a new type of public institution, which held the monopoly of all exchange operations. True, it offered a low rate of interest, but it guaranteed complete security, a rare thing in those days. The bank had already become the cashier of the European continent. It minted its own florins, which were held at a premium, since the Dutch stood solidly behind the issue.

The city of Amsterdam had become the commercial center of the country by the time of the Pilgrims' arrival. There was a lively market in cheeses, herring and tulips to foreign trading places. Its dockyards covered the sea with ships. Then, too, the city supported a newspaper which served as an inspiration to many countries. It also had several publishing houses, the Elsevier House famous among them in the field of literature. Amsterdam was larger than London at that time and infinitely more cosmopolitan, for the Dutch always welcomed political refugees from elsewhere. There were large numbers of Protestants, whose blood had stained the streets of Belgium, France and Spain. To the surprise of many businessmen, the refugees did not detract from the city; rather they helped increase its property by bringing with them their own arts, crafts, skills and trades.

Fine handicrafts flourished, of beautiful objects of wood, glass, tin and brass as well as earthenware and tapestries. Tiles were best made in and about Rotterdam. At first the tiles were used in Dutch floors, but then they moved up until every foot of the walls was covered with them. The Delft blue-ware was world famous.

The two canal boats bearing the Pilgrims entered Amsterdam through the Waag, or weighing house, which had been a key part of Amsterdam's history for a long time. The former fortress was then on the border of Amsterdam. By walking toward the harbor along either side of the canal called Kloveniersburgwal, the large public square, Nieuw-market, was reached, at its center the Waag, built in 1480 as a fortress. As the town's boundary expanded beyond it, it began to be used as a weighing station.

From the Old Church, it was a short walk down the Warmoesstraat to Dam Square, or the Dam, which acquired this name from the wooden dam that was built a thousand years ago to hold back the sea water of the Amstel River. Following the Geldersekade to the harbor, one caught a glimpse of the 15th-century Schreierstoren, Tower of Tears. When the Tower was part of the old wall at the sea front, women and children used to gather there to bid farewell to their menfolk sailing away, and friends and families came to bid goodbye to New World discoverers. Halfway between the Waag and the Tower of Tears, a narrow side street, the Stormsteeg, led to the canalside street called Voorburgwal, where at Number 40 there was the old church known as Our Dear Lord in the Attic, built in the attics of two adjoining canalhouses during the Reformation, when Catholics had to worship surreptitiously.

At the time the English Separatists went to Holland, the Dutch were the richest nation on the globe. Their merchant marine equalled those of England, France and Germany combined. Holland annually built a thousand vessels for trade with all of Europe and the East Indies. The Dutch East India Company had an exclusive charter since 1602 to trade around the Cape of Good Hope, voyages which took two years. It was, in fact, Amanuel van Heteren, born in Antwerp and Minister of the Netherlands to the Court of St. James, who advised Henry Hudson that the Dutch could use a good mariner for its enterprises. In the summer of 1607, Henry Hudson sailed for the Muscovy Company of London in search of passage to China across the Polar Sea, obtaining this expedition as the grandson of a founder of the company. He made another voyage for this company in 1608. On his first voyage, he had tried to penetrate the frozen areas between Greenland and Spitzbergen; on his second expedition, Hudson tried to sail between Spitzbergen and Nova Zembla. Returning to The Hague in 1609, the brave mariner was received with honors.

The welcome the Pilgrims received in Amsterdam was heartwarming. Pastor Clyfton, who had fled to Holland from England ahead of them, was the first to come on board the barge. He was closely followed by the gentle Pastor John Smyth of Gainsborough. Practically all of the deck space was occupied by a large number of the 300 communicants of the Congregation known as the English Ancient Brethren, headed by their Pastor, Francis Johnson, brother of the Pastor of the Brownists then in Middelburg. Their teacher, Henry Ainsworth, and Elder Studley acted as interpreters.

While the attitude of the Dutch was friendly, hospitable and broadminded in accepting people who had different religious beliefs, this did not help the newcomers to understand the Dutch language and to accept the strange ways in which the Dutch worked and lived. They soon realized that in leaving England they had entered a new world. Skilled only in farming, it would be of no use to them in this large city. But they were willing and able.

The Ancient Brethren for their part found it difficult not to sympathize with what the Separatists had suffered in England. Their own young Pastor, John Greenwood, had been executed by hanging in 1587, and their leaders, Henry Barrow and John Penry, put to death in 1593 for religious insubordination. It was in 1595 that the congregation fled to Holland, led by Pastor Johnson. Greenwood had organized the early Separatist movement in 1587 in one of his brief periods away from prison. He was put into that filthy jail in London called the Clink. Johnson who had been expelled from Cambridge University for his beliefs, went to Holland to serve as Pastor to the English merchants living in Middelburg. At the time he was a militant Puritan, intent on correcting the evils of the Church, but opposed to the radical ideas of secession or separation from the Anglican Church.

Johnson bought a small shop, where the tract of Henry Barrow had been printed. He had the Dutch authorities seize the edition of 3,000 copies, which were summarily burned. Only two copies were salvaged from the holocaust. However, when Francis Johnson read one of them, he was so impressed by the contents that he returned to England specifically to visit Barrow in the Gatehouse Prison. In this manner, he became converted to the Holy Discipline. His resignation from his post at Middelburg followed, and he turned his energies to the Separation movement.

Fifty or 60 people fled to Amsterdam after the hangings of Penry, Greenwood and Barrow, and this small group formed the nucleus of the Ancient Brethren. Barrow had bequeathed what little was left of his fortune to the Separatists at Amsterdam. Daniel Studley, Scipio Bellot and Robert Bowle were sentenced to death about the same time for sedition, Bellot and Bowle both died in prison. Greenwood, Barrow and Penry were vilely abused at their trial and subsequently executed. Francis

Johnson spent several years in jail. Henry Ainsworth, who was only 24 years of age when he became Pastor in Amsterdam, at first found work with a bookseller as a messenger and porter, but soon his erudition was discovered. Born at Swanton Morley near Norwich, England, Ainsworth was the son of a yeoman who managed in 1588 to send his bright son to Cambridge. There he studied Hebrew. Later, when he met a rabbi in Amsterdam, he was encouraged by him to continue his Hebrew studies. So it was that while employed at a book store, he began a biblical translation into English from the original Hebrew. In time his works would bring him renown, and his *Book of the Psalms* was used for generations by Pilgrims and Puritans in the United States.

The background of the congregation in Amsterdam is replete with misunderstandings, quarrels, and some surprising human activities. While Francis Johnson was in prison in London, he had married Thomasine Boys, the attractive widow of a Fleet Street haberdasher who had died a martyr to his religion. Thomasine not only had a fine figure, but enhanced it with a whalebone stay corset, and a wardrobe of fine Elizabethan attire. She was given to wearing four or five rings on her fingers and had a sparkling personality. George, the brother of Francis, disapproved of Thomasine. He also strenuously objected when the newly married pair adopted Deliverance, a pretty little girl of five, left fatherless when the state executed John Penry.

The bitter differences between Francis and George Johnson were temporarily suspended in 1587, when the brothers were deported to America. With Daniel Studley and a group of prisoners, they were to establish a colony at the mouth of the St. Lawrence River in Canada. One vessel sank at sea and the other returned to Southampton, whence both George and Francis escaped to Amsterdam. At that time the group originating in London was reorganized and Francis Johnson retained as Pastor, with Ainsworth becoming teacher to replace the martyred Greenwood. Studley and George Knyveton continued as elders. Knyveton had previously been an apothecary in Newgate market in London.

In March, 1593, two years before the London congregation fled to Holland, 50 members were arrested while holding a meeting in the woods outside of London. The gathering was conducted by George Johnson, younger brother of Francis and Headmaster of a school in Mincing Lane. At the meeting was Edward Boys, the successful Fleet Street haberdasher whose widow, after he was arrested and later died of jail fever, married Francis Johnson.

It was only a very small group from the Scrooby Congregation that reached Amsterdam. There were John and Bridget Robinson and their two small children, John and Bridget. William and Mary Brewster were accompanied by their son Jonathan, a lad of 15, and their little daughters Patience and Fear, an infant in arms. William Bradford, 19, lived with the Brewsters. Pastor Richard Clyfton had arrived in Amsterdam from England a year earlier, in August 1608, with his wife Ann Stuffen, and their three sons Zachary, Timothy and Eleazar, nine to 19. The congregation from Scrooby Manor had always been small, not above 50 to 60 members. Those 15 persons named were all who could manage to escape, six adults and nine children under 21. Of the three households, only one was destined to reach Plymouth, Massachusetts—the Brewsters.

John Smyth and his Gainsborough Congregation of 70 to 80 members had arrived a few months before in Amsterdam. John Smyth had been expelled from Cambridge for preaching militant sermons, and his expulsion protested by 70 college fellows. When he refused to leave, he was jailed. Francis Johnson was at Cambridge at the same time. Smyth's group of Brethren of the Separation of the First English Church at Amsterdam was referred to as the Ancient Brethren.

The English people in Amsterdam provided sleeping accommodations for the Pilgrims in the meeting house they had constructed in the Bruinistengang, Brownist Alley, in the heart of the city. The first evening there was a welcoming supper party. However, the arrivals were disturbed to find the Ancient Brethren so worldly in their attire. The newcomers stood among them, faces sober, bodies stiff, in an island of isolation, their resentment culminating with the appearance of Mrs. Johnson, whose rose velvet hood was enhanced by a yellow ostrich plume. She had always had a penchant for gorgeous hats, and history books refer to the quarrels of the Johnson brothers in her regard as the Millinery War. She wore four gold rings on each of her well-tapered hands.

"She smells of musk," Bridget White whispered to her sister, Catherine Carter.

"What about it?" Catherine whispered back.

"Musk! Satan's odor! Look at her stiff lace ruffs. How do they keep standing up so high?"

"Because they are starched."

"But starch is the devil's paste."

"Not in Holland, Catherine. Remember, we came here to find religious freedom. Now we have it, let us allow others likewise to be free in their beliefs and tastes."

"A pastor's wife in England does not dress so elaborately," the other demurred.

"She uses her own money. Besides, Catherine, you should not try to make life in Holland an extension of that in England. Accept the difference in dress here in Holland."

"But," Catherine protested, "it isn't scriptural."

"Again, Catherine, we desired liberty; let's now grant the same privilege to others."

The Pilgrim women found it very difficult to talk pleasantly with a pastor's wife and keep one's eyes away from the richly embroidered bag hanging from her girdle. But what a luscious feast the Brethren had provided for the travelers in the parish quarters! On each table a roasted pig's head served as a fragrant centerpiece. There were fried eels as large around as a man's arm, turbots, the delicious European flatfish, platters of venison and baskets of hot currant buns. Salted ducks, gezouten scharren, were served next to tureens of steaming hot split pea soup. Generous glasses of beer and Holland rum were the accompanying beverages.

The following day, the Brethren tried to find habitations for the Pilgrims, whose funds were very limited. However, after much searching, sufficient rooms were rented—downstairs, upstairs, in attics, in front and in back of houses in the Groenburgwal, Green Rampart, in Doelenstraat, Archery Street, in Kloveniers-Burgwal, Culvines Street, and in the Bruinistengang, Brownist Alley. It meant climbing narrow, winding staircases and sometimes an unaccustomed holding on to a tarred rope in ascent. Most of the rooms rented were simply furnished, but a few had a schouw, a fireplace, and a floor of black and white flagstones.

They were advised to deposit any extra funds in the Amsterdam Bank. As there had been no banks in London for this purpose, it took some persuasion to convince them that they should encourage an enterprise unknown in their native country. Yet the monthly interest would be welcome. Handicapped by lack of knowledge of the language, they had to accept whatever employment was available. Mostly they had to find work in the textile, metal and leather trades at unskilled tasks while learning. William Bradford apprenticed himself to a French silk-maker. Others became wool-combers, twine-makers, candle-makers, hat-makers and brewers. Some of the women could earn a little by doing laundry at home, starching and ironing the high ruffs much in fashion. "That we should have to come down to working on the devil's finery," they complained. One by one they saw their husbands become potters, barrel-hoisters, and vendors of meat and fish, while only a few worked with a goose-quill pen in a counting house or office, or taught English in the evening either privately or in a classroom. Wood carving was much in vogue after 1600, people decorating their homes with many statuettes and other carvings. William Bradford changed from silk-making to wood-carving when a Dutchman offered him a place in his shop, where planks, slabs and blocks were transformed into cabinets, sewing boxes and frames for paintings. While he was there, an order was received for carving the head of a stern John the Baptist, a scowling apostle Peter, and even a whimsical devil. When members of the English Congregation found out what was being carved in the shop, they raised a storm of protest at the next Thursday evening meeting.

"It is a sin," a deacon of the congregation raved at William Bradford. "A big sin to help someone carve heads and faces of wood that cry and laugh, glow with gladness, and cringe with pain. It is unbiblical."

"It is generously paid for," William said in his confusion at being openly admonished.

"As if that is an excuse to help a Dutchman carve a figure of Judas that makes people weep for his perfidy, and a Mary whose virginal beauty catches one's breath. Mocking lips and gleaming eyes don't belong on the walls of people's homes."

"Thus far I have seen the man carve only some banisters for the stairways of a mansion, where the owners have done away with the primitive stair ropes; and . . . and a frame for an ancestor's portrait."

The deacon could not possibly object to carved banisters; but the words "ancestor's portrait" sent him raving again. "Proud and haughty faces! Walls hung with greed, gluttony, lust and fury carved in wood! Holland is altogether too full of such manifestations of worldly living. We know that the Dutch glory in their art, but it is high time for us to show that we do not share in such vain glory."

As a matter of fact none of the Pilgrims even had their portraits painted, with the exception of Edward Winslow, and no personal descriptions survive in their writings. In this they adhered strictly to the Old Testament and its command, "Thou shalt not make graven images."

While William refrained from answering, he prudently kept his post in the carving shop, which awakened his sense of independence. He resolved to oppose any elder or deacon who trespassed on his own personal freedom of earning a decent livelihood. There was no question about it that the Reformation of Martin Luther and John Calvin greatly affected the ways of life of the Pilgrims. Their clergymen commanded them to withhold from any drunkenness or depravity, ostentatious display and all other excesses.

For their part, the Puritans and Separatists tried to adhere to the principles of industry, frugality, and complete dedication to religion. In the field of the arts, it meant disassociation from the worship of material beauty. "Death to every form of art" was the Pilgrims' slogan. In their eyes, a God-fearing citizen worked on a farm or in a factory, in a counting house or in a shop. He associated with his own kind or at most a cabinet maker or worker in copper, but not with an embroiderer nor even an architect, whose occupations were dubious. Questioners of the merit of this edict pointed out that in the Book of Exodus were recorded the specifications for cedar pillars and carved doors with which King Solomon decorated the first great temple in Jerusalem to house the Ark of the Covenant of Moses.

It was also doubtful whether a Pilgrim should work in the field of letters, beyond the printing of Bibles and sermons. If the Bible was the last word in literature, why were other books needed? Music, too, was considered beyond the pale, since ultimately all music led to the worldly pleasure of the forbidden theater and dance hall. With so many fields closed to them by their own beliefs, it was difficult to find acceptable work in Holland. Their skills found few outlets and their accumulated knowledge and experience did not fit the prevailing needs. While Holland enjoyed an era of prosperity, the immigrants from England saw only "ye grime and grisly face of povertie," coming upon them like an armed man with whom they must "buckle and encounter" and from whom they could "not flye."

Nor were they welcomed everywhere, as their assumed rigidity, somber attire and unwillingness to find joy in the good things of life other than food, human love and companionship of family and friends, did not quite harmonize with the Dutch conception of hearty living. Then, too, their air of self-righteousness and spiritual aloofness often excluded ready friendships with people other than their own closely knit group. The Dutch sometimes ridiculed them for their differences in dress and behaviour. Dutch women in Amsterdam, who enjoyed more personal freedom and position, were surprised that an English woman was compelled to wear an embroidered letter of white thread on a piece of scarlet cloth stitched to the bosom of her dress to announce to the world that she was an unmarried mother, which was still the law in England.

The first Sunday they were in Amsterdam posed a decision to be made by the Pilgrims. Where should or would they worship? The young preferred to go to church with the Dutch in the Old Church, Oude Kerk, the ancient edifice first erected in 1306 and which held for them a rare fascination. The older members wondered whether they should go to the new and beautiful Zuider Kerk, South Church, then in the process of being built. Since the main lobby of the church was not completed until two years later, the older men among them decided all should attend church with the Gainsborough Congregation. Just like the rule of the elders in the time of the Old Testament, what the older men decided was accepted as law. The decision seemed to be a good one. They had already been associated with the Gainsborough group back in England, and Pastor Smyth agreed to share his responsibilities with Pastors Clyfton and Robinson, assisted occasionally by Elder Brewster.

Their place of worship was starkly simple. There was no organ and no pulpit, but a plain table was placed on a dais to hold the Bible. The Pastor was attired in black from his skullcap to his shoes and gloves. As prophesying had just then been forbidden, the service was somewhat shorter than usual. The

Dutch city fathers disapproved of the crude arguments that sprang up within the church. They objected to so much turbulence on a Sunday, so free speaking was limited to the Thursday evening meetings.

The two groups at first operated in a pleasing accord, but harmony did not last even through the first Sunday's meeting. John Smyth thundered that the English version of the Bible was not the true word of God, being man-made and therefore tainted with errors. Only the Greek and Hebrew scriptures were divinely inspired. John Wycliff of Yorkshire, England, had translated the Bible from the Latin vulgate into English in 1380-84, and William Tyndale's New Testament was first printed in the English language in 1525.

The Pilgrims' eyes flashed from one to the other in silent condemnation. What were they to do? Learn two ancient languages besides the Dutch that already gave them such endless trouble? They ignored Pastor Smyth's suggestion. The following Sunday he proclaimed another censure. The original Hebrew and Greek scriptures were also man-made, so it would be better not to read the Bible at all, but to depend solely upon the Holy Spirit. Let the chosen ones preach and pray and sing and let the Spirit move.

Pastor Smyth stirred up a further storm of trouble on the following Sunday when he asserted, "None of you have been baptized rightly, because baptism is an act of faith and infants are not capable of participation in such an act. What is worse, there is no properly baptized person in the entire world who could baptize you."

Baptism and the Eucharist had been the two principal Christian sacraments, at the center of the liturgies since the early Church. Especially important was baptism, which was spoken of by the Apostle Paul as a re-enactment of the death and resurrection of Christ. To be immersed in the waters of baptism was to go down into death with Christ; to rise from the waters was to come up into new life with Him. By baptism the

Christian entered through the death of Christ into His Resurrection. The leaders of the secession from the Anglican Church deeply pondered the fundamental tenets of Christianity itself.

Pastor Smyth found a solution to this new problem. He asserted he knew how to achieve proper baptism. He asked his church officers to resign. Then he unchurched the congregation and baptized himself, thus becoming the world's first self-baptized person. Following this, he proceeded to baptize the congregation anew. The scandalized Separatists did not express their criticism in so many words, but that Sunday morning, leaving the church, their downcast eyes and the thin line of their drawn lips spoke more eloquently of their coming decision than the three fiery sermons of Pastor Smyth combined. They would desert such a confused leader, forsake the Gainsborough Congregation, and join another group of worshippers. They withdrew from the church a few days before Christmas Day, and on the fateful day of withdrawal Pastor Smyth himself was excommunicated.

Where to worship next? The younger members proposed again that they go to the Dutch Church, the older men stood firm. No, they would certainly not associate with any Dutch congregation, for surely they would eventually lose their English identity. Some were attracted to the Ancient English Church, whose members had fled to Amsterdam in 1597, but it was apparent that this group would soon be extinct as a congregation. Then there was the Scottish Presbyterian Church, which had been established in the city of Amsterdam in 1607 and was a prosperous, strongly Calvinistic church.

This group had purchased the former Roman Catholic Beguin Church, that little jewel of architecture in the Kalverstraat, in the heart of the city of Amsterdam. But sheer beauty of architecture had little appeal to the Pilgrims, who preferred a bare hall in which to worship. But the Presbyterians were Scottish and not English. Furthermore, some followers of the excommunicated Pastor John Smyth had leanings toward joining them. As it turned out, those members did become gradually absorbed into the Scottish Presbyterian Church. But even today their descendants still worship in the English language in this famous Presbyterian Beguin Church. At that time the Thomas Kelroyn congregation joined the Gainsborough group, but the Pilgrims found them too uncooperative; so during the Yuletide of 1609, they joined forces with the Brethren Church.

Young Henry Ainsworth became Pastor of the Brethren Church succeeding John Smyth. Brilliant, erudite, he had his eccentricities, which the Pilgrims called windmills in his head, from the Dutch *loop met molentjes.* In 1591 he had withdrawn from Cambridge University because of Separatist leanings before he received his degree. In the bookshop in Amsterdam where he found his wages were very low. It was found that he could translate from the Hebrew, and he was called upon to be assistant Pastor at the Brethren Church. He was well liked as dominee, or minister, until it was discovered he had a tile off, as the saying went. This aroused antagonism against him. On his first Sunday he stormed from the pulpit, "Our hymns are man-made. Don't sing them. Only the Psalms of David are divinely inspired and worthy to be sung in our church." The following Sunday he declared, "Leave all of the singing to the men. Let the women remain silent. Let them join in their hearts, but not audibly." The next Sunday he announced from his pulpit, "Part singing stands condemned as frivolous. Let no man indulge in it. Organs are the devil's bagpipes. Do away with them. If you want music, use the instrumental kind. It alone is fit for worship."

William Bradford smarted with indignation at his dictatorial tone, as if the man were an oracle! He himself did not have the gift of the spoken word. "I have not the ready vocabulary others have," he used to say. "They use words that come hard to me." But Henry Ainsworth's unusual behavior offered Bradford an incentive to retort, so at the end of the Sunday's service he rose and asked quite belligerently, "If our hymns are

man-made, what am I doing in church? For sing I will. Pre-
destinated or not. Sing I will!" It was the challenge for which
Ainsworth had waited. "I have set to work to put the Book of
Psalms into metre and rhyme," he replied.

"In English?" William demanded.

"And in Dutch," Ainsworth answered in cool, measured
tones. "For that is our future language."

A murmur of protest, then an icy silence followed. No one
dared to express an opinion on this point.

"Contemporary melodies are profane," Ainsworth continued extenuatingly. "I have already selected 39 tunes out of ancient Dutch folklore, and I am simplifying them to reduce their
tempo to slow stateliness."

We'll see, William thought, but he refrained from asking
further questions. Stubborn once his mind was made up, he
overcame his timidity to ask at the following Thursday evening
meeting, which was led by Elder William Brewster: "Are the
young among us going to sing those queerly rhymed Psalms?
Pastor Ainsworth may be a Hebrew scholar, but I am told he is
a crude poet whose verses are tortured and make the Psalms
lose much of their meaning."

The older people among the congregation looked annoyed.
Until that moment William Bradford had been liked for his
amiability. Had he now joined the discontented young people
with new ideas? There it was again: Holland was ruining the
meekness among their boys, turning them into young men of
conviction, who wanted to break the chain of their dogmas.

"Are we going to sing those twisted tunes?" William persisted. "They may be ancient now, but I have been told that
once they were mere dance tunes and popular ditties. All they
are good for is making the Dutch laugh at us."

"William!" Elder Brewster scolded. "William Bradford,
what has come over you? Stop rousing our young people into
further revolt."

"Freedom," said William Bradford, "surely includes our singing, too."

Bradford stared at William Brewster's clothes. They were colorful on that Thursday evening, and much more elaborate than the prescribed black of Sunday. "You may think it frivolous of us that we want to sing hymns instead of queerly rhymed Psalms, but we call it frivolous of you to come to our meetings dressed in a coat of red velvet with a ruff of starched linen fluted around your neck. And . . . red silk hose and . . . carrying a walking stick with a bow on it!"

Brewster defended himself mildly. "I have to go about dressed·as a teacher. I have to earn my living teaching English and Latin."

A deacon turned his head toward William and coughed meaningfully to stop him. William caught the hint and kept silent. Elder Brewster merely smiled. He was not even annoyed with William's ranting, for he liked the lad. Yet it was an indication of what was happening to their young people in Holland. Some of them, like William Bradford, Bartholomew Allerton and John Robinson, insisted upon worshipping at times at the Scottish Presbyterian Church. And wasn't there a community of Roman Catholic Beguins living next door? It was as if those boys took perverted delight in the fact that the Gregorian songs of the Beguins were clearly heard when the Presbyterians sang their Psalms. Wasn't it whispered that off and on, and in all secret, those Beguins held services inside of the church? Didn't the sanctuary smell of incense? Didn't the city fathers, by some misplaced leniency, allow deceased Beguins to be buried right in the churchyard? Their bodies even lay openly in state in front of the altar. What was worse, visitors were encouraged to come in to see them by the offer of free wijn en koek— wine and cake—for all. Then twelve zusterkens, sisters, carried the coffin in procession around the court, and the Beguins took spades and dug a grave.

Everyone knew that the Beguins were not actually nuns, but devout Roman Catholics who were allowed to live next door to the Presbyterian Church. They usually kept their doors halfway open, so that any English women and children who wished could freely walk in to visit them in their monastic life. Following the Reformation, all Roman Catholic priests had been put in boats and driven from the city of Amsterdam to villages which had remained Catholic. It was indeed a grim time in religious history.

The preaching about Jesus Christ in the early Church centered on the glory of the Resurrection, representing Christ's victory over death. Realistic representations of the crucifixion were unknown until the fifth century. It was not until the end of the 13th century that attention in Western Europe turned from the triumph of Christ to His sufferings. In the following centuries, emphasis was placed more and more on the human suffering of Christ and His mother. Suffering is a lonely experience, tending to turn people in on themselves, while joy is an emotion to be shared.

There was much piety and melancholy in the period which finally culminated in the Protestant Reformation, very likely resulting from the loss of the joy and triumph over death of the risen Christ. Martin Luther placed his accent on the theology of the cross, negating the theology of glory, in response to the gloomy mood of his own times. This was a far cry from the early Church, in which the structure of the liturgical celebration and the pattern of the liturgical year were based on the Resurrection, Easter evoking the emphasis which later was placed on Christmas.

In Amsterdam, where Catholic services were forbidden, the door of the little Beguin church was sealed with a heavy iron lock. This lasted for 29 years, until in 1607 the burgomasters sold the church to the Scottish Presbyterian congregation. It was during that time that the Beguins became known as kloppers, knockers. They would induce some wandering priest to come into the city to hold services, and went cautiously about knocking at the doors of devout Catholics, whispering the place, day and hour of the meetings.

Theirs was an old society, dating back to the Middle Ages, when men went on holy crusades to Jerusalem. Lambert de Beguin, a priest, founded the order to care for the widows and girl orphans who earned their keep by sewing, embroidery and manual home labor. They were held in high esteem for their devotion, capability and meekness. But the people of Amsterdam were shocked when the sons of the English Separatist group insisted on going to the church of the Presbyterians, next door to that of the Beguins.

The situation in Amsterdam among the people from England was fraught with drama before the Middelburg group arrived. There was the quarrel of Francis and his brother George Johnson, who had so mercilessly criticised Francis' wife Thomasine for her colorful apparel and gay ways. Thomasine could not forget George's meanness and refused to let him live with her and Francis in the parsonage meeting house rented on the Green Rampart. The family quarrel reached a climax when Francis excommunicated his brother and publicly told him "to go to the devil." The human drama had a poignant moment when the aged father was urged to come to Amsterdam from England to make peace between the brothers. The elder Johnson crossed from Yorkshire, but for his pains was also told by Francis "to go to the devil" in defiance of the laws of hospitality, to say nothing of the commandment to honor your father and mother. The dismayed parent laid his trouble to sending his sons to study in the University, but he did take George home with him, where he was soon jailed as a rebel. George died in Durham Prison, where he had undertaken the writing of a monumental manuscript, interrupted on page 214 by his untimely death.

In 1604, the year of Queen Elizabeth's death, when Pastor Thomas White came from his parish in the west of England with a dozen members of his congregation, he could not get along with the Ancient Brethren and withdrew to form a church of his own, and some of the discontented Brethren also withdrew from Pastor Francis Johnson. Thomas White published a book, which included a protest against the amorous involvement of Elder Daniel Studley and Mrs. Judith Holder. Daniel was also said to be involved with his wife's daughter. Ruling Elder Studley brought a legal action for slander against Thomas White to a Dutch magistrate, who ruled in White's favor, and the church, meaning Francis Johnson et al, was charged with paying the court costs. White had included in his printed broadside that the church of Francis Johnson was only a "brokerage of whores". It did not refer to Thomasine, who had modified her ways and become suitably matronly in her role as pastor's wife.

To add to the furor, Christopher Lawne published a tract blasting the Brownists or Separatists. These bitter quarrels were a scandal in the city of Amsterdam. Daniel Studley was indeed a different man now than he had been 15 years before, when he was the trusted confidant of Greenwood and Barrow in England and had escaped the country only by grace of a commuted sentence. His character underwent a drastic change in the Netherlands. He was a man of wit and charm, who enticed the love of pretty Mrs. Judith Holder and other attractive women, but Judith had other loves, too. There was Geoffrey Whittaker, who boasted of his amatory prowess until ultimately he and Judith were both excommunicated.

Studley was involved with Marie May, who kept a tavern and sang bawdy songs to entertain her guests, and he also tried to win the favors of the young daughter of Henry Ainsworth. All through his various escapades, Francis Johnson refused to believe that Studley really was a rascal. He stood loyally by him up to this last accusation, which was the breaking point between Johnson and Ainsworth, for after all Ainsworth's daughter was only a child. Christopher Lawne used the best of his Elizabethan English to lecture Studley, calling him a "beastly swine, a night crow, a slippery eel". Studley worked as a master at a school conducted by the Ancient Brethren, and the children's parents complained that he taught the children to sing wicked songs, which they said he had learned from Marie May. He answered this accusation by readily admitting all his sins, and blandly promised that he would, however, reform.

As for Pastor John Smyth, who, with a friend from Gainsborough, had formed a church called Brethren of the Separation of the Second English Church at Amsterdam, he caused great concern by his startling pronouncements about the Bible not being properly translated and the error of baptism. He and his group tried to join the Mennonite church but when they were rejected, they took quarters in Jan Munter's bakery, called the Great Bake House. Such were the circumstances before and after the Englishmen reached Amsterdam from Middelburg, and which ultimately led to their decision not to settle in that city.

Chapter 7

CHRISTMAS IN THE NETHERLANDS

Amsterdam was a gay city. Around its fruit stalls, fish stalls and public wells gathered the young sons of the Separatists to exchange jokes and stories, and sometimes to ridicule passersby. Often the youngsters focused their gaze on a soldier with long halberd or a fowler with his clapnet, people so different from any they had known in Scrooby. The callers-up, or knockers-up, with their long pole to knock on the second-story bedroom windows were, thought the English youths, just the ones who could rouse them early for a morning prayer meeting. Vendors, ballad singers, sleighs pulled by horses over the packed-down snow of the street, and boys with swarms of pigeons, all diverted their attention.

As Yuletide approached, young Bartholomew Allerton drew attention to himself when he announced his intention to marry a Dutch girl he had fallen in love with. He not only earned his own keep but also had a little extra money to spend, and, like the rest of the Allertons, spent it the way he wanted to, regardless of the opinions of deacons and elders. The Separatist group disapproved of Bartholomew seeking a spouse outside of their own flock, yet dared not say so openly lest they offend their Dutch hosts.

Bartholomew liked to walk with his fiancée along the rampart and in the Kalverstraat. He sometimes took her to dinner in a tavern of the town on a Saturday evening, instead of remaining quietly at home in preparation for the Sabbath.

165

How pleasant it was for the young people to enjoy the tavern's culinary specialties as a change from the daily fare of stew combined with pea soup, the one-dish dinner their mothers prepared in large black iron pots in the open fireplaces. Beef at the tavern was broiled and flavored with fennel seed. Netherlanders enjoyed using rare spices, in which they traded so heavily with the East Indies. A fine carp was a special treat, served with mixed greens of lettuce and chervil, dressed with sorrel juice in the Dutch manner, whereas the English favored the use of saffron. Porcelain tableware was already being used in Dutch homes and taverns, as well as forks and linen serviettes.

The engagement of the young couple was announced in the Dutch way. Bartholomew arrived in a carriage on the appointed day at the home of the young lady, the coachman's hat and whip both decorated with little bouquets of white flowers. The bridegroom-elect was attired magnificently for the occasion: a short yellow satin coat, bordered with brown fur, topped his breeches, and a splendid ostrich plume decorated his widebrimmed hat. His high leather boots had yellow heels, which resounded as he climbed the steps of the high stoop.

"I have a little surprise for you," he said after greeting his fiancée and her mother. They opened the small packages at once. In the mother's was a sewing box beautifully inlaid with mother-of-pearl. In the daughter's small box was a plain gold ring.

"Put it on your finger," he said. "Put it on your left hand in the fashion of your country, and change it to your right hand at the wedding ceremony."

Bartholomew's parents were shocked that their son had sanctioned his engagement with a gold band, a devil's circle! They belonged to the Elizabethan age, their children were growing up in the time of the independent Dutch. The Dutch wore high fashions, which contrasted with the Separatist women in their black or charcoal-grey dresses set off by white aprons. The future wife of Bartholomew Allerton came to the Sunday's meeting in a bonnet of pink taffeta and a bowed dress with a rather modestly extended hooped skirt. Some of the Dutch girls wore the hoops so extended they had to move sideways through the door. They also dusted their complexions with a little flour.

The engagement customs of the Dutch were a far cry from those of England. When a young man called on a girl to declare his intention of marriage, the interior of his hired carriage was provided with silver hooks on which to hang little sheafs of flowers. At each home of friends or relatives where they stopped to announce their engagement, the future bride was given a little bouquet which she hung on the hooks, a charming custom indeed. Flowers, seen everywhere, were a way of life with the Dutch. They were brought to the city in the early morning by low-lying flower boats.

The English refugees thought the city with its gay ways was a whorish Babylon, and did not hesitate to say so, especially preachers from the pulpit, even when Dutch people were present. They naturally preferred their own uncomplicated village life in England. Foreign ballad-singers and clowning tumblers annoyed them as much as the puddles in the Amsterdam streets.

Squawking birds of exotic plumage from far-away lands did not impress them particularly. Neither did a vainglorious Dutch nobleman followed by an entourage of pages in livery. They disdained dropping a courtesy to the first lady of the land, riding by in a gilded coach upholstered in red velvet trimmed with golden tassels. They would make sure not to observe her. Amsterdam, indeed, was entirely too worldly for their simple taste. The new houses, springing up everywhere, were not of the solid masonry of their own country mansions. The walls were not three feet thick but merely one, they did not have iron bars at the lower windows to make people feel safe. Dutch people were more daring in taking risks, and were not even apprehensive of the dark. They no longer wanted a home to be a fortification, but preferred fragile glass window panes without iron bars, glass windows a boy could shatter with a stone from his sling shot!

The people of Amsterdam were internationally minded, and the wealthy enjoyed great elegance. As an Englishman, a Separatist could never feel at home in a mansion that had satin drapes from France, mirrors from Florence, marble from Genoa, and carved cabinets from Naples. The English preferred their furniture to be made not of teakwood from India but solid English oak. But a Dutchman was ostentatious. He might sit on velvet brocaded chairs, sleep on down, wear a fine waistcoat from Flanders embroidered with red poppies, a vest from France embroidered with Oriental yellow dragons, Spanish hose of peach color silk, and a pair of great trousers stuffed and stiffened with horsehair to such a width that he had to sit on a bench—a chair could not hold him. Blue garters were bedecked with golden buckles, a silken bag would hang from a man's leather waist belt, to which sometimes was buckled a rapier.

The Englishmen found the customs of the Dutch strange, and even tackled the social problems of the city from the pulpit. They condemned publicly the thrifty custom of having four sturdy dogs instead of a horse pull a little wagon with merchandise. Dutch thriftiness contrasted strangely with opulent living. Just as Puritans opposed the frivolities and excesses of the Anglican Church and the Separatists to such an extent that they withdrew entirely, they criticized their Dutch hosts with firmly set lips and controlled any show of their own emotions in a display of self-discipline. Love between them was expressed by courtesy and consideration. Pastor Clyfton preached: "Tokens of affection publicly displayed are immodest. Please refrain from unseemly expressions." Even the girls and women rarely kissed each other, except in meetings and partings of importance. Love between men and women was considered private and sacred, and no less ardent simply because they were small farmers, humble artisans, weavers, carpenters and blacksmiths, accustomed to the hardships of life.

In Amsterdam they were sorely tried, oppressed by the difficulty of earning a livelihood. The Puritans and Separatists had turned away from the holidays of the Anglican Church, as celebrated raucously in Elizabethan England. They repudiated Easter, great symbol of the risen Christ, and the observance of Christmas, birthday of the Christ child, even insisting on regarding December 25th as a working day. Soon after their arrival in Amsterdam, the Christmas season was upon them, but they decided not to participate in the holiday spirit evident everywhere.

Though the mystery of Christmas lies in the deepest desire of the human heart—the universal yearning for spiritual renewal and refreshment, for escape from the hardships and fears of the world and cruelty of time—the Pilgrims despised it. They did so because they knew the idea of celebrating on or about December 25th was born thousands of years before Jesus Christ, in Mesopotamia, whence it journeyed to Greece and Rome and up the Danube River valley to the warrior tribes of the frozen north. The last days of December were the time of the winter solstice, when the sun dwindled and the powers of darkness seemed to be gaining ascendance over the forces of light. On December 25 the sun began to reassert its power once more and to give new promise of a bountiful harvest. In Rome it was known as Dies Natalis Invicti Solis, the birthday of the unconquered sun. The Greeks and Romans reasoned that the last days of the year were a struggle between the gods of the upper world and the monsters of chaos and night. To propitiate the darkness and revitalize men, feasts spread from temples to homes, and gifts were given, not only to the gods, but to friends and family; and work ceased so people could renew their strength. Bringing in the Yule log was a colorful tradition in medieval Europe, not just in England. The custom came from the winter festival of pagan Norsemen, who believed that smoke and fire, along with horns, shouts and other loud noises, would frighten away witches and evil spirits. It was toward the end of the fourth century that the celebration of December 25 was chosen to counteract that of the Roman Saturnalia, which set loose a tidal wave of moral chaos in uncontrolled debaucheries. The Bishop of Constantinople, St. John Chrysostom, remarked in one of his sermons: "On this day the birthday of Christ was lately fixed at Rome in order that while the heathen were busy with their profane ceremonies, the Christians might perform their sacred rites undisturbed."

In Holland, apart from the Christmas celebration, December 5 was the occasion for exchanging gifts in honor of St. Nicholas, who made his entry from Spain. St. Nicholas, the Archbishop of Myra (now Demre) in Turkey, born in A.D. 345, was the patron saint of sailors, pawnbrokers and children. He traveled far and wide giving presents to the poor. Gradually his legend drifted north and merged with the myth of the god Odin, another wanderer, who drove reindeer and judged the deeds of men. The Dutch called him Sinterklass. He checked on the behavior of children and brought the good ones presents in a sleigh. St. Nicholas had a great white beard and was dressed in a sweeping red robe, his head adorned by a red and gold mitre, and he carried a bishop's golden crook. He was attended by his Moorish servant, *Zwarte Piet*, Black Peter. Weeks before St. Nicholas Day, the shops displayed goodies of marzipan fondant, *speculaas*, spiced ginger cookies, *taai-taai*, spiced cake in the form of animals and other figures, great chocolate initials nine inches tall, banketletters, pastry filled with almond paste, and little windmills made of sugared pastry. Because St. Nicholas was a patron saint of mariners, there grew up a tradition of putting out little wooden ships to greet him. In the lower Rhineland, on both sides of the Dutch-German border, instead of these ships, children began to set out their wooden clogs, always by the fireplace, because this was the one way a midnight visitor could enter a tightly locked house.

The cold, howling winds of the north brought to the Christmas season a mixture of joy and dread. To defend himself against the creatures of the winter darkness, the northerner was wont to fill his home with ivy, holly, yew, pines, spruce and fir. These were among the few growing plants that did not lose their green in the desolation of winter, so they were believed to have some special power against the witches and demons. Smoke and fire, enemies of cold and darkness, were used long after the north became Christianized, so that the Yule log of the pagan era continued to be burned ceremoniously.

The English refugees were familiar with the revered greenery of mistletoe, which bore its fruit in winter and was prized for its curative powers. In pagan times it was cut each November by the Druid priests in stately and solemn procession and distributed sparingly among the people, who religiously hung it over the doors of their houses. In medieval England, it was customary to carry a bough of mistletoe to the high altar of the church during Christmastide, and hold it up before the congregation while the authorities proclaimed a "public liberty, pardon and freedom" to all local criminals, who were sent away from the town with a kiss of peace. By the end of the 17th century, the old tradition had evaporated and mistletoe meant kissing loved ones and friends.

Christmas was a time of color and joy in Holland. Most homes were still made festive in the ancient tradition, with a wooden pyramid decorated by candles and glittering ornaments. In some homes, however, a Christmas tree replaced the medieval pyramid, a tree made joyful looking with candles, oranges and pieces of colorful candy. Pope Gregory the Great (A.D. 540-604) had never heard of a Christmas tree as such, but he enjoined missionaries not to destroy such pagan customs as were devoid of harm and in accordance with the tenets of the Church, but rather to weave them into the fabric of Christianity. Similarly, many of the old pagan gods and goddesses were transformed into male and female saints of the Church. It is generally believed that the first Christmas tree was of German origin dating from Saint Boniface (A.D. 680-754), the English missionary to Germany, who replaced the sacrifices made to Odin's sacred oak by a fir tree, the tannenbaum, adorned in tribute to the birth of the Christ child.

The Separatists called it "ye Devil tree," and would have nothing to do with it. Homes were decorated with cypress, red-berried holly sprigs, and laurel. Green has long been associated with Christmas, but the idea of a tree bedecked with symbolic flowers and fruits incorporates an ancient legend that on the first Christmas Eve, all the trees and plants of the forest burst into bloom to celebrate the miraculous birth of the Christ child. The first written evidence of anyone using a tree to celebrate Christmas comes from a forest ordinance of Ammerschweier in Alsace, dated 1561, which declared that "no burgher shall have for Christmas more than one bush of more than eight shoes length." And in a travel book written some half century later, mention was made of "Christmastime in Strassburg where they set up fir trees in the rooms and they hang on them roses out of many colored paper, also apples, wafers, gilt sugar and so on."

Christmas became a family holiday when children would gather around the Christmas tree to hear their father read from the Bible the well known story of the first Holy Night and the three wise men. Many beverages were enjoyed. The Spaniards had learned of chocolate in Mexico in 1517. A traveler, Antonio Carletti, learned how to prepare a chocolate beverage while visiting Spain in 1606, and is said to have brought the secret home to Italy, whence it quickly became popular with royalty and the wealthy. Anne of Austria carried the taste for chocolate with her when she went to France to become the bride of Louis XIII. Chocolate drinking was not introduced to England until 1657; apothecaries ground it like a medicine in a mortar with a pestle. Tea came to Europe in 1610 in Dutch merchant ships from Japan, and the Dutch were to become the first tea drinkers of the West. It did not reach England until 1664. The Dutch East India Company brought it directly from a part of China called Amoy, where it was called t'e, pronounced tay. Coffee had been introduced into Europe from Java around 1600. The Dutch, at their coffee houses, enjoyed the beverage sweetened with honey and enlivened with spices, especially the rare and costly cloves. Rich people mixed cloves, cinnamon or sugar with ambergris in their coffee. Ground cardamon seeds were also used.

At Christmas time hot spiced wine was served from bowls, bedecked with garlands of ivy and red ribbons. There were wines, French brandy, Holland gin, English rum and Scottish liquor, which the Separatists considered good English drinks. Food was heaped on the festive board in abundance: roast suckling pig, a boar's head, roast goose, pheasant and capon. Every Christmas season meal was a miniature feast, with a great variety of dishes. Whatever remained was given to the poor. For more than two weeks of festivities people entertained family and friends, exchanged presents, and played games of hat-cockles, blind-man's buff and hunt-for-the-slipper. Gambling for money was forbidden in a Christian home, but cards were shuffled and dice clinked across the table. Wasn't it Christmas, the time to be jolly and merry for young and old? But the sojourners from England didn't believe in Christmas, regarded by the Puritans as a heathenish observance no longer officially celebrated in England.

The answer of the Separatists to Christmas was to withdraw themselves from it, wanting no part in the never-ending conflict between the spirit and the flesh at Christmas time. Deep in the human soul is the desire to renew hope at the low time of the calendar year, and many people seek it in food, drink, and the joys which money can buy. Over the centuries, the best of the old traditions have been retained, as humanity gropes toward the light emanating from the star shining in Bethlehem.

Many of the practices of Christmas have descended from the Dutch by way of the English and French. Christmas in

Holland was a family observance, intimately connected with the ceremony of breaking bread together and feasting. England had its Christmas or plum pudding. Holland had its oliekoeken or Dutch doughnuts, made with seedless raisins and brandy; jan hagels or Hollanders, made of butter, sugar, egg, flour and chopped pecans; and pitmoppen, butter-almond cookies.

And Christmas in Holland was a wonderful time to go skating. But the Pilgrims did not approve of skating, nor did they sanction riding in a sleigh, gay with red and silver trimmings, pulled by beplumed horses. Was there anything more glorious to watch than skating and sleigh-riding in Amsterdam? But the Pilgrims would not express approval. Portly sinjeuren, gentlemen, in puffed breeches of vivid hue and wide-legged boots with red heels, paraded "flaunt-a-flaunt" along the quay with ladies in their scarlet cloaks. Prosperous men wore great velvet coats trimmed with fur, while laborers intermingled with them freely, wearing leather jerkins and woolen caps pulled over their ears. Row upon row of men, women and children glided gracefully over the ice. Winter joy always comes to the hearts of the Dutch people when the waters freeze hard. How happy the women looked seated in their colorful sleighs, tucked cozily under fur blankets while the men held the reins for a smooth dash across the ice. Gleefully they called out greetings to each other. The Dutch temperament paradoxically thaws when the thermometer drops below freezing. Shifts of ice-sweepers busily cleared snow from the ice, as many a skater good-naturedly threw them coins of encouragement.

Pastor Robinson and his wife strolled by on the bank to watch the busy scene. He swept off his beaver hat with the elaborate flourish of his time to greet a passerby. The Pastor himself was entranced by the ice sport. Surely this pastime would be taken up by many in his congregation. So ice sports were not to be condemned entirely, it seemed! He looked on as a man laced the straps of his wife's skates, and then the couple glided away, heads bent forward, he leading as if in the dance, she holding onto his hands folded behind him. With long strokes they sailed gracefully across the expanse of ice.

"Now," the Pastor asked his wife, "how could I preach against such domestic bliss?"

"How could you?" she agreed. "To make your appraisal complete, let us have a cup of hot aniseed milk in one of those little tents there on the ice."

They entered the large milk-stall a little shyly, somewhat conscious of being observed. It was crowded with festive people. They stayed for a while, drinking one hot aniseed milk, then another, enjoying several pieces of the famous Dutch gingerbread. A violinist and a flute player went from table to table, and like the others, Pastor Robinson contributed a few pennies to the musicians. Then a jester, bells jingling from his wrists and ankles, ran in, also soliciting pennies. He stopped in front of Pastor Robinson, seeking to tell his fortune. John did not understand what the man requested, but his Puritan training automatically made him shake his head in the negative. Bridget, his wife, blushed a little, and the two quickly left the milk-stand.

It was only a small incident, but their failure to understand the language passed like a shadow across their happiness. No, life in Holland was not going to be easy for them. And what would their children do? How would the young in the Pilgrim group react to so much gaiety and temptation, and the pitfalls concealed beneath innocent-seeming joviality? The boys had girls had already made up their minds about one thing: They would skate, and their parents could no longer hold them back, though they did impose a single restriction. The boys could go skating as long as they refrained from competing in any sport. So they went to the ice, skates hidden under their jackets to prevent a reprimand by more strict church members. Once they reached a canal, on went the skates and off went the boys, that is, after a day or two of trying, stumbling, falling and trying again.

Soon they were ready to compete with any Dutch boy.

The fourth day John and Isaac Robinson, Love and Wrestling Brewster, Bartholomew and Remember Allerton, and a number of other Pilgrim boys went skating at the Waterland with a group of Dutch youngsters. To the consternation of their parents, they stayed out all day. It was exhilarating, skating across the Dutch pastures, passing close to well-built farm houses scattered haphazardly over the endless fields of foot-thick ice. They did not give their anxious parents a thought until nightfall drove them home at last. Then they had to face the stern rebuke, long prayers, and the dictum to "stay away from those ice-skating Dutch boys."

Coming home with their cheeks glowing, the English children met the scoldings with disappointed silence. They yearned to be accepted within the Dutch group. "The ice is making little freebooters of the best of them," their parents lamented. "Skating makes them independent. What are we to do? How can we cope with the strong influence here in Holland?" And before long, even the girls followed the boys in exerting their efforts for more freedom in this new country.

The next day the English boys went to the picturesque Isle of Marken in the Zuiderzee, where the people wore their own traditional costumes. Their houses were built on earth mounds, on which the wooden piles were plainly visible. They watched with interest as the men sat making wooden shoes. But while the new surroundings proved to be pleasurable for the youngsters, their parents had a difficult time making ends meet. They had to work long hours for a bare living in Amsterdam, mainly because they were classified as unskilled laborers and therefore ineligible for membership in the coveted guilds.

It was impossible for some to accept their reduced status in life, and these left stealthily "between the moon and the milkman" for Germany across the Rhine, hoping life there would be easier somehow. Some returned to England, although they knew they would be severely punished or imprisoned for their religious disobedience. Others were quite successful in Holland. Honest and dependable, although poor, the group secured credit from baker and butcher. The Dutch people employed as many as possible, for they were conscientious, capable and temperate.

Various circumstances involving religious politics ultimately converged to force the group to leave Amsterdam for a smaller Dutch city, where the wanderers would settle for a long period before being stirred onward to the New World.

Chapter 8

LEAVING AMSTERDAM

There were many reasons why the Separatists decided after a year's sojourn not to settle permanently in Amsterdam. It was not the loneliness they suffered, which would follow them no matter where they went outside of England, but they could not cope with foreign ways of life. They missed their English farms and crops, their occupation with animal husbandry. Accustomed to little country villages along the Ryton and Idle Rivers near Scrooby, they found the Netherlands overwhelming. The cities were crowded centers, fortified and walled, guarded at all times by armed troops, so the Dutch citizens could move about with confidence in the conduct of their urban lives.

In Amsterdam, the English found it difficult to adapt to planning, pushing, organizing their routines. It was not easy to peddle fish when they had never done so before, to come home with their hair, body and clothing reeking with its smell. It was hard to drive a wagon all night to empty indoor privies, with their nauseating odors. Who could whistle and sing while hauling clay for a potter who made statuettes of an idolatry they disapproved of? It was humiliating to become the sweeper of an inn, the general choreman and hoister of barrels. Worst of all, in Holland the children seemed to pull away from parental authority and the principles one treasured. They were confused by the stance assumed by the parents in their secession from the church and state of the country where they were born. Now they were merely two religious groups in exile, some Puritans,

179

some Separatists, each cordially disliking the other. The Separatists and the Ancient Brethren who had preceded them to Amsterdam could not exist in harmony side by side. For one thing, the Separatists wanted to go further than holding religious services. Like the Puritans, they were in favor of reform, but they were also overcome by the sins of the modern world.

They conceived of a new social order based on the equality of all men. Their God was the God of the Old Testament of the Hebrews, a mighty Jehovah, a God of wrath. To them the Bible was not a promise but a threat. Hell was a real place which was very much at hand for wrongdoers. So impressed were they with the proximity of hell that some Separatists invaded Dutch churches and shouted, "Woe, woe unto you! Turn away from your worldly ways. Damnation is at hand!" The Separatists admired anyone who dared to preach boldly and straightforwardly from the passages of the Bible, especially those aimed at the destruction of sinners. However, the Committee of Burgomasters held different views, and ordered the trespassers not to invade and disrupt the services of the Dutch Reformed Church.

Their own private lives were closely directed by the Bible. They lived by the rules of the Old Testament, following a theocracy which closely resembled the principles of the ancient Hebrew nation. The men cut their hair in an approved fashion, and wore the old-style, unbecoming beaver hats; the women always wore starched white aprons over their black or charcoal-grey dresses. The high hats of the men and the aprons of the women set the group apart and provoked the ridicule of ignorant observers, to which they seemed blissfully immune. The censorship they imposed upon themselves was extreme. Everyone and everything was scanned, monitored by a system of frank eavesdropping which developed into an art among them. There was no compunction about reporting an overheard conversation to the elders. They did not regard it as bad manners or an invasion of privacy.

It was a usual practice for men and women to be brought before the elders of the church on charges such as lying, swearing, loose talking, heavy drinking and adultery. If a woman wore a corset supported by whalebone to improve her figure, this was openly rebuked in church meeting as a sin of vanity. Punishments were meted out at the meetings in the form of harsh words from the pulpit, so that the ideal of sanctification of the congregation's members could be achieved. Those who complied in all ways were entitled to be known as saints. They took a certain pride in telling others outside of their circle that they differed in their beliefs and customs, such as repudiating a religious ritual for the covenant of marriage and for funeral rites. Most of all, they disapproved of celebrating the Catholic and Anglican church festivals of Easter and Christmas, purposely going to work on these holy days. And they condemned those who did not believe as they did.

However, in their own way they enjoyed themselves very much, maintaining close friendships in the group, falling in love, marrying, and remarrying when a spouse died. They enjoyed good conversation and did their share of drinking. People in Queen Elizabeth's time and thereafter drank copiously. Beer for breakfast, punch for lunch, and port at dinner were customary, and in between meals, for a price, there were always brandy, sherry and madeira. There were cold drinks and hot drinks, and children partook of alcoholic beverages from the age of seven.

One reason the Separatists did not get along too well with the groups of Puritans who had come to Middelburg and Amsterdam from England was that the Separatists were mostly simple country folk, with the tastes of small farmers. Among the Puritans were many of the gentry, who had attended college, and there were some scions of wealth and influence. However, there were points of similarity. The Puritans desired changes in the Anglican state Church, while the Separatists were revolutionaries who had abandoned the church completely, so that in essence they were guilty of treason against the state. In England church and state were united so that the religion of the King had to be the religion of his subjects.

Both Separatists and Puritans were people who lived by the precepts of the Bible. Both were English in their feelings, feasting and fasting, entertaining and being entertained, playing games and sports, loving and hating in the robust English manner. It was the only way they knew, and they were by instinct strongly set against any un-English customs. They expressed themselves in the earthy, vibrant language of the Elizabethans, which called a spade a spade.

It was while they were still in Amsterdam that William Bradford began to feel the need to have a voice in decisions affecting the destiny of the Separatist group. His youthfulness strained at the leash of authority, rebelling against the dullness of it all. Born and baptized in Austerfield, Yorkshire, he was about 20 years of age in 1609, when the group lived in Amsterdam. He had become an orphan at seven and lived with his paternal uncles, Robert and Thomas Bradford. Desperately feeling the need for his parents, he was afflicted with a long illness, probably caused by his bereavement. During these years when he could not play as other children, he became preoccupied with reading the Scriptures. He and another young boy walked eight miles every Sunday to Babworth by way of Scrooby to enjoy the preaching of the Rev. Richard Clyfton's illuminating ministry. This was really the first step toward William Bradford's later "fruitful walk with God" for the rest of his eventful life as Governor of the Plymouth Colony in Massachusetts.

At the tender age of twelve, he had already shown a religious bent, and was asked to join the Separatists or Brownists when he was 16. He was included in the group attempting to escape to Holland but who were betrayed by the Captain of the ship they hired. Bradford, indeed, was one of those who spent several months in prison after the incident. Reasonable, brilliant, affable, William Bradford had within him the seeds of leadership, which in time would make him Governor, held in the highest esteem and respect.

With solicitude, William Brewster noted the young Bradford's inner struggle and soul searching. While sitting quietly at the table after dinner, Brewster said quite suddenly: "Come out of yourself, William. Come out of your mood of gloom."

"But what am I to do? It seems we are already defeated and going nowhere."

"We are far from defeated," Brewster replied with a confidence he did not really feel. "You can express your ideas at our meetings," he suggested kindly.

"How can I? You know that I lack formal education enough for that."

"All right, let us take an example. Look at your plate, William. You did notice what you were eating, didn't you?"

"Of course," he smiled in puzzlement, "mussels, a very tasty mussel stew, the food of the laborers of Amsterdam.

Brewster sensed the depression of his answer.

"Well, do you think of yourself as lower than a mussell?"

"Of course not!"

"Yet a mussel got his start in life in a more difficult way than you have been called upon to do. Let us, for the sake of argument, consider its conception. It is very interesting, you know. The female mussels release their stream of generative cells into the open ocean, and no sooner has the flow of eggs begun than the male mussels contribute their own stream of milky sperm. There is such an abundance of it the waters become noticeably clouded. Then dozens of sperm cells cluster frantically about a single female egg cell seeking an impregnating entrance. And do you know what happens?"

"Logically, I suppose only one cell can succeed," William answered, becoming interested in Brewster's theorem in spite of himself. "The rest of course die off, the unused sperm cells and unimpregnated female cells."

"Yes, perfectly spoken. Now the one successful cell faces an almost impossible task. It must propel itself with astounding force through the waves of the ocean fighting against high tide so as not to be cast upon the beach to die, so day by day it swims about in utter aloneness, an infinitesimally lowly bit of life. What to do? Slowly it follows the law of its species and grows a protective shell with one aim, to survive and to grow into its predestined potential."

William listened with loving attention, looking at Brewster's earnest face. The loneliness he had felt dissolved. The Brewsters were indeed his own family as much as if they had been blood kin. He had received from them only kindness and love, and experienced a definite sense of peace in their home.

"Then and only then is the mussel rewarded," he heard Brewster say. "Remember a hundred, a thousand, perhaps a hundred thousand other little mussels have failed to live, but of the number who have survived, he is one. So full of the confidence of living, he becomes leader of all the young and weak mussels and guides their prodigious number into seaweeds among the rocks, where they remain until they grow stronger. Again he takes the lead to become the first to emerge. The other mussels all follow him and leave their home in the seaweeds. You know the ancient tale, how one by one they bind their shells to a jutting rock in the sea by a tangle of threads spun from their claws, just as their leader mussel has done. Soft, yet tough, the threads and accompanying growth of moss hold them secure against the rush of oncoming waves and the eternal drag of the surf. So, packed solidly together about their leader, neighbor with neighbor, kin with kin, they survive in their strong mussel colony. So, you see, William, nothing is too unimportant and nobody too lowly to take his place in God's scheme of creation."

It was after that little talk and the sincerity with which it was imparted that William was inspired to take his full place within the group. From that day on, he began to express himself more freely at the Thursday evening meetings. At one of these he noticed, as he faced the people to speak, that a small girl watched him intently, not so much listening to his words but drinking in his face with her eyes. She was only a child, perhaps ten, more probably twelve, and he flushed at her admiration. For a few meetings thereafter, he observed her stealthily in his own turn. What was the strange spell which held him to her? Was it because of her shy glances from lowered lids? This was the youthful attachment William Bradford made in Amsterdam with Dorothy May, whose father, Henry May, had come to Holland from Wisbeach, Cambridgeshire, as one of the Ancient Brethren. In Amsterdam since 1598, he had become an elder in Henry Ainsworth's church. After leaving Amsterdam, William Bradford returned from Leyden many times on various missions, and saw the young girl for the following four years, until at 16 she would join him in marriage in Leyden.

William Bradford's personality changed as he matured into the paths of leadership and responsibility. He began to visit a Dutch church intermittently, to the distinct displeasure of the elders, because he loved the torrential style of rhetoric practiced there. In England, the Anglican Church had always minimized the importance of the sermon, but in the Netherlands, sermons were composed with much serious preparation, welded point by point into a convincing, logical deliverance. A good Dutch sermon was like the production of a symphony by an orchestra; it ran the whole gamut of emotions. Bradford began to learn by heart parts of these impressive sermons, and use them as asides in his talks at the Thursday evening meetings. The formerly retiring William now held the attention of his admiring audience quite skillfully by rhetoric and logic, and sometimes they detected tears in his voice in the good Dutch style of the time, which was very convincing. Forsaking the stately formality of his English contemporaries, Bradford's talks became little masterpieces of structure and language.

There had always existed a mutual understanding between

himself and William Brewster, and after each Thursday service, the two walked home companionably, drifting together for a bit of spirited conversation.

"You quite startled me, William. You used the word 'democrat' tonight. Surely that was a mistake?"

"No, it wasn't. The word is freely used in Dutch sermons," Bradford returned.

"But, it is an insult to call anyone a democrat and you are aware of that.

"Yes, in England, but not over here in Holland."

"The Dutch are freebooters, William. They don't believe in authority. They want to rule themselves.

"And so do I," said the young man.

"Not in our church, surely. We have our minister to govern us."

"In Holland the elders rule even over the minister. The elders are chosen by the people by ballot."

"By ballot? What is that, pray?" asked Brewster.

"Originally, a little ball was used for secret voting. Now it means voting by a written slip of paper which only the tellers are allowed to see."

"Our people won't want to vote that way. They want to vote by a show of raised hands in our own, old way."

"They'll change in time. I am going to see to it that at our next election of church officers we, too, vote by ballot. I am glad we are growing milder." William Bradford smiled.

"Milder!" Brewster expostulated the word as if it were the town crier's warning of danger. "We are doing no such thing."

"I mean doing away with the dance craze which we once practiced in England . . ."

Brewster now sighed in relief. He was glad young William did not mean they were growing milder in dogma.

". . . and the belief that deafness is caused by witches and the tossing and pitching of our ship in the brine when we came over from England."

Naturally William Brewster was pleased that Bradford had overcome his former shyness and now spoke up at the lecture evenings, but it pained him that he raised so much controversy. He had focused his attention, for instance, on the attire of the wife of Pastor John Robinson, and raved at one of the meetings that she wore velvet hoods with a bow on top and a great hat with an ostrich plume, not to mention a lace fringe at the bottom of her dress and long, gauntlet gloves. "I have seen her throat plainly displayed under a white lace handkerchief. She is being Amsterdamified by the brainless Dutch ladies, and our English women are following in her footsteps. Are we men slaving from dawn until dusk that our women may change from linen to velvet? Is that worth drudging for? Is that civilization? Let us return to the simple things of life. Let us be free from the dictates of fashion."

They found winter days in Amsterdam very cold. Amsterdam . . . with its anciently laid out narrow streets and its houses leaning toward one another. Nor did they like living indoors, even if that meant the women no longer had to cook in a yard, as they did in Scrooby, and sweep their outdoor cooking place with a bundle of twigs serving as a broom. Englishmen who had to deliver things in Amsterdam could not find their way about, names of houses were so much alike—The Gray Elephant, The Young Elephant, the Fat Elephant. How were they to remember where people lived? That the city fathers were planning to number the houses was no consolation for the present. They had no faith in the good will of city fathers, nor in that of any government. More than anything else, though, it was the constant contention and quarreling among the English groups in Amsterdam which filled them with dismay.

"Our settling here is a failure, a total failure!" William Bradford complained at one of their meetings. "Shouting accusations from the housetops! Publishing of violent books and pamphlets! Have you seen the latest book, just published by Christopher Lane? It is called *Ye Profane Vice and Schism of Ye*

Brownists. We give too much publicity to our sins. It would be better to leave this city and begin anew somewhere else where we shall not be hindered by other English groups who are averse to us."

Go away! Again! Now where? William Brewster knew Leyden, which lay about 25 miles overland to the southwest. He liked it there. Scarcely one-third the size of Amsterdam and not having the latter's great maritime traffic, Leyden was still a busy city of some 80,000 people. It was a flourishing center of handicraft industries, and therefore offered many opportunities for employment. More important to the Separatists' frame of mind, it was one of the spiritual capitals of Protestant Europe because of its famous university, established in 1575 to commemorate the people's heroic defense of their homes, lives and religious faith against the armies of Spain which besieged it in the name of the Holy Inquisition.

In February 1609, William Brewster was appointed to call upon the Council House of Leyden to seek permission to settle and work in the city on behalf of 100 men, women and children. John Robinson presented the petition to the Burgomaster, identifying the group as "members of the Christ Reformed Church." This indicated they had been joined by a number of the Ancient Brethren. The Burgomaster replied in a letter dated February 12, 1609, that the town fathers would welcome all "honest persons provided such persons behave themselves." However, the English Ambassador suddenly protested their petition, complaining that "certain Brownists were leaving Amsterdam" who were still fugitives from English justice. But with truce prevailing between Spain and the Netherlands, the weight of English influence had lessened.

Before long all the arrangements were completed. About 200 of them would go. However, at the last moment, Pastor Richard Clyfton decided to remain behind in Amsterdam. It was at this juncture that the group elected their assistant

Pastor, the youthful John Robinson, as their Leyden Pastor, and William Brewster as their ruling elder for life.

On May 1, 1609, as the countryside blossomed into a beautiful Dutch spring, the group departed from Amsterdam for a new life, gathering by dawn with their bundled belongings at the sea dike, where a low-lying boat awaited them. Travel by water was easier and less expensive than by road, so they went the long way around. They sailed up and out the Zuyderzee and down the coast to the mouth of the Old Rhine, then up the historic river six or seven miles to the quays at Leyden, in a voyage which consumed a day. With a cry of delight, they noted "a fair and beautiful city and of a sweet situation." Indeed, it was a fair city with its splendid old buildings and clean houses, broad streets paved with brick, many shaded squares, and canals lined with linden trees and spanned by many gracefully-built stone bridges. Here was their new home.

Chapter 9

LIFE IN LEYDEN

In the Province of South Holland in the Kingdom of the Netherlands on the Rhine, Leyden today lies 18 miles by rail south southwest of Haarlem, 10 miles from The Hague and 35 miles from Utrecht. It is also connected by rail with the seaside resorts of Katwijk and Noordwijk. In the early 17th century it was a busy commercial center with a population which by 1640 reached 100,000. Even in the time of the Pilgrims, Katwijk was a fishing village and a favored seaside resort.

Two branches of the Rhine River enter Leyden on the east and unite in the center of this ancient town, called by the Romans Lugdunum Batavorum. At the close of the 15th century, its weaving establishments were very important, generally manufacturing broadcloth. After the expulsion of the Spaniards from the land, Leyden cloth, baize and camlet were familiar terms throughout Europe, these industries flourishing until the 19th century, when the manufacture of baize was finally abandoned. However, the manufacture of carpets and woolen blankets and the printing business remain Leyden's most important industries. This picturesque old city, where some cobblestoned streets are so narrow two people can hardly pass each other, still has a very active trade in butter and cheese.

In the days of the Separatists, the town square, normal in size, was named Van der Werf in honor of Burgomaster Pieter Van der Werf, who led the defense of the city against the Spanish siege of 1574. The vast open park of present-day Leyden

191

was formed when the explosion of a powder ship in 1807 destroyed hundreds of houses, including that of the Elsevier family of printers at the junction of the two arms of the Rhine where the old castle De Burcht still stands. This ancient circular tower was built on an earthen mound in Roman or Saxon times.

The two surviving old gateways a visitor may note were built at the end of the 17th century and not known to the Separatists, but the Hooglandsche Kerk or Church of St. Pancras was familiar to them, having been built in the 15th century (and restored 1885-1902). The Pilgrims also knew the Dutch Town Hall of Leyden, known as the Gemmenlandshuis Van Rynland, built in 1596, restored in 1878 and still standing, but the old weigh house built by Preter Post in 1658 was beyond the time of the English Pilgrims. However they knew the now-ancient gymnasium built in 1599 and also the timber house, Stads Timmerhuis, built in 1612, both the work of Lieven de Key (1560-1627).

Many industries flourished when the English came to Leyden, chiefly handicrafts, and much work was performed in the home, such as washing, dyeing, combing and weaving of wool. Leyden citizens were often affluent merchants. Many great halls did not cater to noblemen but to the common people, some as assembly places for the guilds.

It was a city full of haunting legends, which at the same time enchanted and depressed the Pilgrims. Its burghers had fought hard for their religious freedom and political independence. Would these Englishmen, too, be called upon to sacrifice so much? Would the truce so recently arranged with Spain, remain in effect? In 1609 a truce of twelve years had been signed at Antwerp, Belgium, by which Spain recognized the independence of the Dutch Republic of the United Provinces. Prior to this truce, during 40 years of wars, artisans and laborers of Belgium had fled to England, Germany and the cities of Middelburg, Rotterdam and Amsterdam in Holland. Each of the contracting parties to the truce kept the territories then in its possession. The Netherlands enjoyed a revival of letters, mathematics and art with the cessation of hostilities. It was the time of the great painter Peter Paul Rubens (1577-1640), famous for his painting *Descent from the Cross* and his numerous pupils, Van Dyck, Teniers, and the Flemish school.

Of immediate concern to the Pilgrims was what would occur when the truce came to an end. Would their sons be drafted into the Dutch military service? Would they as well as the Dutch have to support troops and fight the armies of the Roman Catholic Church? Some 36 years ago, on October 31, 1573, under the rule of King Philip II, Leyden had been besieged by the Spaniards, who fought to bring its rebellious citizens back into the Catholic Church. The Spanish Commander Valdez opened the siege with an army of 8,000 Spanish soldiers; inside the city walls there were no defenders save a small corps of freebooters and burgher guards. The besiegers did not take the city by storm, preferring to win it by a war of attrition. The city was insufficiently provisioned to withstand a long siege, so famine walked the streets from May to October of 1574.

On June 6 the city was placed on strict food rations, and the inhabitants relied on the ingenuity of Prince Willem of Orange to save them. In July, with the consent of the population, he cut the outer sea dikes to flood out the invading Spaniards. Unfortunately, a wind from the east caused the water-level to lower rather than rise, and the Dutch flotilla lay motionless in too shallow water. The Spaniards were able to stand firm while for weeks on end the stubborn wind remained adverse.

Meanwhile the encircled Leyden inhabitants were reduced to hunger. Trees were stripped of their leaves for food. Deaths were frequent, and watchmen on their nightly rounds found many entire families that had perished of starvation and pestilence. The cost of life was great. Some 8,000 people died during the long siege, as day by day the exhausted but heroic survivors climbed upon the walls to hold off the Spaniards.

At last deliverance was at hand. On the night of October 1, a violent storm arose and suddenly shifted the wind to the west, piling the sea high on the coast. The farmers' homes, goods, cattle and land were ruined. The ocean swept through the broken dikes and dashed its waters furiously landward toward the walls of the city. Prince Willem's fleet of low boats was ready, and in storm and darkness the sailors rowed and poled toward Leyden. Wherever the water was too shallow, they shouldered their boats and walked. Then a strange, fierce midnight battle ensued. Never before had the Spaniards fought from the decks of their ships among chimneys of submerged farm houses and orchard trees. The Dutch sailors easily sank the Spanish vessels, hurling the crews into the waves and swimming after them to fling their harpoons. In defense, the enemy attacked the Dutch with boat hooks and daggers. But the Spanish fled in panic at the very moment they might have tasted victory: a part of the city wall collapsed and provided them a long-sought entrance but they were routed by the crashing stones.

On the morning of October 3, 1574, almost a year after the siege had started, Leyden was relieved. The quays were lined with famished people as the little Dutch fleet rowed toward them through the canals. Barrels of bread and herring were immediately thrown from every vessel to the eager throngs. And to this very day, the people of Leyden still recall the lifting of the Spanish siege on October 3 by eating dark bread and salted herring.

Their first act after deliverance plainly reveals the living religious faith of Leyden's citizens, as magistrates and burghers, sailors and guards, women and children formed in a solemn procession and walked to St. Peter's Church, where on bended knees they gave thanks to the Lord. But when they tried to close the service with a hymn, overcome with weakness and emotion over their salvation, the congregation burst into tears and all wept together like children in sorrow and joy.

To commemorate their heroism, William the Silent, on

behalf of the Republic of the Netherlands, gave the burghers a choice between ten years of tax exemption or a university for their town. The burghers preferred a university, which was inaugurated on February 5, 1575, endowed with a handsome revenue. Originally, the University of Leyden was located in the Convent of St. Barbara, but was removed in 1581 to the Convent of the White Nuns on the site which it still occupies, although the building itself was destroyed by fire while the Pilgrims were in Leyden, in 1616.

Now Leyden set the standard for universities to follow by making Latin the language of instruction. Thus students of every nationality were able to take part in the revival of learning that developed such men as Hugo Grotius, the founder of international law; Christaan Huygens, the physicist; and Anton von Leeuwenhoek, the first to study microscopic organisms. Leyden's professors were soon renowned all over Europe for their learning, integrity and independence of thought. It was the proximity of the University and the many students the Pilgrims took into their homes to board which helped to liberate many of them from their dogmatic conceptions. From its inception, the University provided special evening courses for adults, a rare thing in those days and unknown in England.

The group coming from Amsterdam settled near Pieterskerk, or St. Peter's Church, formerly a massive Catholic Cathedral in the center of the old part of the city. From the Breestraat, the narrow, bustling street which forms the backbone of old Leyden, past the 17th-century facade of the Town Hall, all that remains of the ancient building destroyed by fire in 1929, a left turn down the street beyond brings you to the covered Cornmarket Bridge, from which there are magnificent views. Further along is the Burcht fortification, the 11th-century mound on the hill, the 14th-century Hooglandse or St. Pancras Church, and the old St. Anna Almshouse.

The narrow street called Persijnhofje that continues downhill from the entrance to the almshouse, leads across the

Rapenburg Canal to the University. The library, laboratories, lecture halls and other buildings are in this area. A left turn as you leave the University takes you along the Rapenburg Canal past the Museum of Antiquities, on the other side, and back to Breestraat. Another walk from St. Peter's leads down Herensteeg, past a house with a plaque indicating that this is where William Brewster lived and his Pilgrim Press published the theological writings that conflicted so strongly with the dogmas of the Church of England. Proceeding across the Rapenburg Canal along Doezastraat to the Witte Singel, you come to the small museum of the Pilgrim Fathers.

The Brewster family lived on Stincksteeg, Stench Lane, where they lost a newborn child, and where Bradford lived with them until his marriage to Dorothy May. As mentioned, when the Separatist Church was organized in 1606 in the Manor at Scrooby, William Bradford, then 16 years of age, joined at once, much against the wishes of his apprehensive relatives, who had reason to fear for the young man's safety. The following year, Bradford was one of the group who tried to flee from Boston, England, to Holland, and was taken prisoner and jailed for several months. However, in 1608 at Grimsby, William Bradford was one of the first passengers to board the readied Dutch ship which was blown by a typhoon to the coast of Norway, and after the storm subsided, made its way to Middelburg in the Netherlands.

In 1611, at the age of 21, Bradford came into a "comfortable inheritance" from his parents' estate. He contributed a generous portion to the Leyden church, and also bought a house on the Achtergracht, which he would later sell to stake the proceeds on the adventure to the New World. He proposed marriage to Alice, a daughter of Thomas Carpenter, but fickle Alice, who had encouraged him sufficiently to buy their future connubial home, suddenly accepted another suitor as her husband, the well-to-do Edward Southworth, with whom she returned to England. This was a great personal disappointment to young Bradford, who believed himself terribly in love, and he matched his somber face with bleak-colored clothes. Yet youth cannot be long suppressed: At the most unexpected moments he appeared quite the gallant in a red vest with silver buttons above tight knee breeches, a handsome violet cloak, a broad-rimmed blue felt hat, and white silk stockings.

Within two years his erstwhile sweetheart, pretty Alice, was just a receding memory. He joined his hand and heart with Dorothy May, now 16, in December 1613, when she traveled alone from Amsterdam to wed him in Leyden. In due time a son was born to them in the fine house on the Achtergracht.

Earning a livelihood was hard in Leyden. Many of the Separatist group, as we saw, devoted themselves to carding, cleaning, dyeing and combing wool at home. As in Amsterdam, many could not qualify as full-fledged craftsmen for membership in the labor guilds, so the physically robust became porters at inns and wagon-loaders at the breweries, and the less strong, makers of ribbons and gloves and carvers of wooden house signs. Some, who had enough money to buy an initial supply of sundry goods, became itinerant traders in notions, such as needles, thread, knives and scissors. They avoided occupations like helping strolling players, jugglers or numerologists, and declined to work for painters and sculptors, disdaining art forms as idolatrous. However, brewing and pipe-making were considered Christianly occupations; and so was barbering, barbers being expected to have some knowledge of practical medicine and surgery. At length most of them attained a competent and comfortable living through hard and unrelenting labor.

Records in the Leyden archives for 1610 reveal that William Bradford became a maker of fustian, corduroy or moleskin, thick-twilled cotton cloth used in clothing for Dutch laborers, and then in the serge-like fabric used for fine clothing. Nor did he neglect his education, attending evening classes at the University to learn Dutch, French and Greek, and to continue his studies in Latin. Applying himself with diligence, Bradford learned to read the Bible in Hebrew, quite a linguistic achievement. Originally an earnest follower of John Calvin, with the Calvinists' somber ideas about God, sin, hell, redemption and salvation, Bradford became more liberal in his thinking, leaning toward the Dutch Reformed Church of Leyden. He occasionally worshipped there instead of with his own group.

Jonathan Brewster, now 16, became a ribbon maker; others found employment as finishers of bombazine and other cloth, silk-workers, felt-makers, button-makers, drapers, tailors, hatters, glovers, leather-dressers, cobblers, metal-workers, carpenters, cutlers, brewers, barbers, stone and brick masons, hod-carriers, printers and pipe-makers. Working hours were from sunrise to sunset, wages were very low. Brewster's fortune by this time was greatly reduced, and since he had a large family, he was glad to get students from the University to tutor in English and Latin.

Martin Went became a candle-maker; Thomas Richard a weaver; Edmond Williamson, baize-worker; John Reynolds, printer; Bartholomew Smith, pipe-maker; William Buckran, hat-maker. George Morton became a merchant; Julius Julian, carpenter; Samuel Fuller, who was physician to the group, became a silk-maker. Guthbert Guthbertson worked as a ribbon-maker; James Kingsland, tailor; John Jenny, brewer; Henry Wilson, pump-maker; Zachariah Barrow, twine-maker; and Roger Seymourson became a mason.

John Carver, a leading member of the group, astute in business matters and quite capable of making "ye goodlie fortune," successfully transferred his equity from England to Holland. He, too, was generous in extending his funds to help the Separatists flee from Scrooby to Holland, and continued assisting the less fortunate while in Leyden. He contributed generously to the upkeep of their meeting place, and was eventually to invest heavily in the plan to finance the group's passage to America.

Born in Nottinghamshire, not far from Scrooby, John

Carver was a business man in London before joining the radical Separatist movement. His wife, Catherine, was a sister of Mrs. John Robinson, the Pastor. He was a man of few words, who knew how to make his plans materialize. Regarding England as his mother country, John Carver had little patience with those among the group who later became Dutch citizens, although he realized this was a necessity in order to belong to the guilds. In 1609, he helped lead the Scrooby congregation in its flight to Holland. In Leyden, he was appointed deacon, but from 1617 to 1620, he actually spent more time in England than in Holland, organizing the emigration to New England. Carver, in fact, originated the idea of sailing for America and establishing an English colony there.

The Leyden group showed a strong clannish spirit, restricting their friendships for the most part within the congregation. On their first Sunday in Leyden, Pastor Robinson laid down certain rules as a guide for conduct. All members had to forego contact with Dutch churches. They were not allowed to meet with non-Separatists in Dutch homes, not even for prayer or Bible reading. And they were to abstain from taking Holy Communion with the Dutch. The young people protested so vehemently that the next Sunday, Pastor Robinson hastened to state that he did not disapprove of the tenets of the Dutch Reformed Church. If anyone felt the need for it, he added, he might pray and read the Bible, not only with the Dutch, but with members of the Scottish Presbyterian Church at Leyden as well.

There was no reason for the Pilgrims to feel lonely in Leyden. There were 135 other English refugee families—soldiers, merchants, laborers and scholars—around them. In all, some 10,000 British subjects dwelt in Holland during that time. They lived under a national religious establishment that tolerated all faiths. They enjoyed the liberty of unlicensed printing and the benefits of free schools for their children. They could buy, hold or sell land, which they could not do in England. They lived in a land where deeds and mortgages were registered.

For the first time they enjoyed local self-government, with its town meetings, written ballots, municipal representation, courts and schout—district attorney. They lived under the Dutch United States, which had a written constitution and a motto, "In Union there is Strength," and whose flag was red, white and blue.

Feudalism had taken a weaker hold in Holland than in any other country of Europe. In Frisia, original home of the Anglo-Saxons and the largest province of Holland, feudalism had never even been known. The walled cities, so much more numerous than in England, acted as municipal republics, fortresses of local freedom. The Dutch were the first to reverse the ancient principle, *cuius regis, cuius religo*, that the people must be of the same religion as the ruler, and declared that the ruler must be of the same religion as the people. They were the first to accept the principle of no taxation without consent of the taxed. They were also the first to teach open revolt against despotism, and that the government existed for the nation and not the nation for the government. In fine arts, music, painting, civic architecture, inventions, industry, navigation and political science, the Dutch were among the leaders of Europe. They were the first to practice wood-engraving, reform the calendar, abolish witchcraft, and use the pendulum clock, telescope, spectacles and many other modern comforts. Holland had the first system of common schools in Europe. The Bible was translated into Dutch as early as 1477. No other nation in Europe was so saturated with biblical discussion, a fact which explains the religious history and political energy of the Dutch.

Contemporary England presented a marked contrast with Holland. With a population of two-and-a-half million, only one-fourteenth of its arable land was cultivated. The remainder was wild land, great stretches of marsh and fen and woods filled with game. Garden vegetables were still unknown in England, and for centuries the only industry had been wool, which had to be sent to Holland to be woven. Only one kind of farming was practiced—grain cultivation. Clothes were mostly of home-spun wool; finer apparel came entirely from Holland. Even the first rough woolen cloth was not woven in England until, in 1331, Dutch weavers were imported. Such luxuries as brick houses, underclothing and table linen were known only to the rich, although common in the Netherlands. Indeed, the ordinary name for body and table linen was "Holland linen."

At the beginning of their stay in Leyden, the Separatists' religious meetings were held in any home large enough to accommodate as many as 200 people. But the young folks looked with admiration at the handsome 12th-century Cathedral of St. Peter, in which facilities for religious services had been offered to them without charge. A feeling of awe filled their souls as they gazed at its graceful lines and symmetrical architecture. The Cathedral almost seemed to have a soul of its own embodied in stone and mortar. Its fascination took root in the heart of William Bradford, and even young John Robinson and others felt its spiritual impact. They sometimes went there to worship, much to the aggravation of the older people. The young men's obstinacy was "mete with" by the Pastor and elders and nipped in the bud. The elders could be "stiff and rigid" and were exceedingly so with those spreading tales of the evils done by others who were yet "remiss in themselves." Some of the group avoided "virtuous conversation," while others were quick to gossip, having little else with which to amuse themselves.

On the whole, however, they enjoyed delightful society and spiritual comfort together, as William Bradford was to recall many years later in his *History of Plymouth Plantation.* As to the strifes and quarrels which sprang up among them, they were relatively slight, and even the Magistrate gave them commendable testimony, averring "Ye untruth of ye strife is richly made of slander believed by ye few, being raised by ye malice of some."

Not until in May 1611, did the group acquire a permanent

meeting place. The large old house which faced the south side of St. Peter's Cathedral, known as the Green Gate, Groenepoort, had been the stately mansion of Mynheer van Poelgeest. It was in the heart of the old city, in Bell Alley, Kloksteeg. Once a spacious home of gentility, it had a large reception room or salon, and could readily provide for a parsonage. The house was purchased by the congregation in January 1611 for 8,000 guilders, one-fourth down with the signing of the deed and the remainder to be paid in installments of 125 guilders a year. There was a vegetable and flower garden in the rear of the house, and a space about 50 yards square walled on three sides, the open side fronting on the Dark Canal, Donckergrafte. In this area they erected 21 small houses, each two-and-a-half stories high, for some of the congregation.

It did not take the Pastor and his wife long to move in with their children, John, Bridget and Isaac, and their maid servant, Mary Hardy, who followed behind, according to custom, carrying as many bundles as she could. The dedication of the meeting house was a time of great rejoicing, somewhat jarred when Elder Brewster turned the festive gathering into a meeting by clapping his hands for attention and announcing, "I have a proposal to make. Now that we have our new church, I want to propose that we stop smoking during the services. It is not the smoke I object to, but all the noise the flint and steel make in lighting our pipes."

A menacing silence followed. "What is there against our smoking in church?" one of the members asked in wonder. "With the services lasting four hours, a man has to do something to be occupied."

"Let the custom die a natural death," Dr. Fuller suggested.

"Don't force us to give up our habits," young Turner said. "We want to be free. We don't hanker after new ideas."

The young people smiled ironically to see their elders in dispute. They often spoke up at meetings, sometimes raising their voices, but the elders ruled. Many of the boys and girls were of "ye beste dispositions, ye gracious inclinations," while others were determined "to get ye reins off ye necks." The manifold temptations of prosperous and free Holland drew them away from strict adherence to rules. Some of the English boys became Dutch soldiers, others took to the sea, much to the grief of their parents.

The elders settled all kinds of personal problems in public after the Sunday morning service. Sometimes women grappled with one another, pulling each other's hair and horrifying the men. In this way they fully made up for remaining silent at meetings. They interspersed compliments with such outcries as "slattern" and "slut", or "I'll tear the clothes off your back, you hussy."

People counted the months of pregnancy, and if a child was born seven months after a marriage, it was in good form to be indignant. The innocent infant would be referred to as "the child that shamed the congregation." Pastor Robinson often had to decide delicate cases, for which he was well qualified, conducting a loving and prudent ministry, his care always for the welfare of his flock. In many ways he was like a father to them, sagacious too in business matters, and he gave wise counsel. Such was the mutual esteem, it was difficult to judge whether he delighted more in them or they in having such a good Pastor. He was, indeed, a man of singular virtues, sharp wit and solid judgment. He was utterly sincere and hated any hypocrisy. He was also an expert disputant, achieving a reputation as foremost preacher in the city of Leyden of his time. In disputation and in writing, few were his peer. He became a student at Leyden University and later served as professor of English and theology.

Pastor Robinson preached three times a week, twice on the Sabbath and again on Thursday evening. All had learned the sad lesson of dissension in Amsterdam and tried to maintain harmony among themselves and to cooperate with their Pastor. Brewster was elder, Samuel Fuller, serge-maker, was deacon.

and apparently had been the leader of the seceding Ancient Brethren of Amsterdam.

On the morning of the Sabbath, the meeting began at 8 a.m. The men sat on one side and the women on the other; the children were in a group by themselves. During the service the members kept their heads covered, whereas the Dutch prayed with uncovered heads. The Dutch also seated the families together at their church services instead of "decently" separating the women from the men. Nor did the Dutch ministers wear the sign of respect, black gloves.

The service opened with a long prayer with the congregation standing, then Pastor Robinson read passages from the Bible and elucidated them. Then a psalm was sung unaccompanied, since the organ was outlawed by the Separatists as the bag-pipes of the devil. When Henry Ainsworth's *Book of Psalms* was published in Amsterdam in 1612, it was adopted for use in the singing. The Pastor did not preach from a pulpit but stood on a low dais which supported a simple little wooden table to hold the large Bible. After the sermon, which lasted up to two and a half hours, another hymn was sung, and the deacons passed the plate for contributions, which ended the service about noon, after a brief benediction.

The congregation then walked home for their midday meal and reassembled for the afternoon meeting, which was devoted to prophesying. The meeting opened with a short prayer, a chosen text was read and then the discussion was begun among the men, as St. Paul had said it was "not meet for women to have a voice in the church." In Amsterdam, Pastor John Smyth had been reproached for allowing women to speak their thoughts.

The records in Leyden are clear in naming several of the original group from Scrooby, England. There was Roger White, brother of Bridget, wife of Pastor Robinson, and of Jane White, her youngest sister, who married Ralph Tickens in 1611. In London Ralph had been a mirror-maker. In the same year,

Elizabeth Neal of Scrooby married William Buckrum in Leyden; he was originally from Ipswich. Then there were George and Thomas Morton, sons of a Catholic family who lived at Harworth a few miles up the Ryton River from Scrooby, as well as the Mortons' neighbor, Francis Cooke, of the hamlet of Blyth. George Morton, who had been a merchant in York in 1611 married Juliana Carpenter, sister of the wife of Deacon Fuller.

William Brewster witnessed the 1610 wedding of a Miss Hanson of Scrooby and William Pentus, a fustian-maker originally from Dover. Also from Scrooby were Robert Peck and his sister Ann, who lived with the Brewsters as their wards, and the Southworth brothers, Edward and Thomas. Edward, who became a silk worker in Holland, was married in 1613 in Leyden to Alice Carpenter, daughter of Alexander Carpenter, who had come from the hamlet of Wrington near Bath as one of the Ancient Brethren separating from the Church of England.

These are the only people, along with the Robinsons, the Brewsters and William Bradford, reaching Leyden who can be connected with the old Manor House at Scrooby. The group of 21 included four small children. It is all the more remarkable that, under the leadership of Robinson and Brewster, the church of the Separatists in Leyden increased until it had some 300 members. Nor was the Robinson congregation the only English church in Leyden. A year before the arrival of the group from Amsterdam, the Scottish Church was organized. This was an English-speaking unit of the Dutch Reformed Church situated near St. Peter's and the Green Gate. The two groups were amicable and even took communion together at times, which once was a grave offense, but Pastor Robinson had become more tolerant after the dreadful fiasco of Amsterdam.

Among those who became citizens in Leyden, and thereupon eligible to join the guilds for skilled workmen, were William Bradford, who was naturalized in 1612; Jonathan

Brewster in 1617; Isaac Allerton, the tailor of London, and his brother-in-law Degory Priest, a London hatter; Richard Masterson, woolcomber from Sandwich; Thomas Rogers, dealer in camlet; and John Turner, merchant.

It was late 1616 or early 1617 that William Brewster was able to establish a publishing house, assisted by Thomas Brewer of the Kentish gentry, who was described by the English Ambassador to the Netherlands as "a gentleman of a good house, and of good lands." Brewer at 36 was 16 years younger than William Brewster. He had settled in Leyden several years before the Pilgrim group arrived, and purchased a large home known as the Green House, Groenhuis, a few doors down from the Green Gate in Bell Alley. Since several students from the University lived there, it naturally became an intellectual center. Thomas Brewer registered for classes at the University. In Leyden he became a Calvinist, joining the Scottish Church while maintaining friendship with both Mr. Robinson and Mr. Ainsworth.

As partners in the publishing enterprise, Brewster and Brewer set up an office in Choir Alley, the Koorsteeg, actually a part of Brewster's house, the other side of which fronted on Stench Lane. They brought over from London a master printer, John Reynolds, and Edward Winslow, a bright 22-year-old. Winslow had met the Leyden congregation during his tour of Europe as a wealthy man's son. Evidently he knew John Reynolds well, because shortly after his arrival, he was a witness at his wedding. Edward Winslow's mother, Magdalen Oliver, was a Londoner, but he was born in the west of England, near Worcester in the hamlet of Careswell, the eldest of five sons and three daughters. Edward was the first to adopt Separatist ideas.

Three books were published by the new firm in a few months' time. The first was a translation into Dutch about the ten commandments; the second a translation into Latin about Calvinism. These initial publications served as a smoke screen for the real purposes of the house. The English Ambassador,

Sir Dudley Carleton, complained when the firm published the *Perth Assembly*, which was an attack on King James I and his bishops for their suppression of Scottish Presbyterianism.

William Brewster of Leyden was accused and a search made for him. He remained a fugitive in Holland and England until he embarked on the *Mayflower* for America. Thomas Brewer was arrested and detained in the University of Leyden. He managed to get out of this scrape, but many years after he returned to Kent, he was arrested by the authorities for having preached while in Holland "in ye houses, barns and woods, that the Church of England is the whore of Babylon and the synagogue of Satan." He was confined to prison for 14 years on the grounds that he was a Brownist in conflict with the state Church of England.

Pastor Richard Clyfton had decided to remain in Amsterdam, and Elder Daniel Studley had called those going on to Leyden "ignorant idiots." Francis Johnson was also angry and frustrated at losing at least one-third of his church membership. It was a bitter omen before the final collapse of his church.

It was customary to cite verses from the Scriptures in support of any kind of argument. Five words from Matthew, chapter 18, verse 17, ". . . tell it unto the church," provoked controversy. This passage referred to the injunction of Jesus that if one of the faithful brought injury to another, the matter be exposed before the church for its decision. But, it was asked, who was the church? Henry Ainsworth held to the views of Robert Browne, and Barrow claimed it was the congregation, but Francis Johnson said it was up to the elders to decide any moot point. William Brewster was sagely in favor of compromise. It was Johnson who broke the accord by demanding Ainsworth and his group go to Leyden, which they obstinately refused to do. After the Pilgrims left for Leyden, the Ancient Brethren, once the brave vanguard of the Separatist movement, came to an end late in 1610.

The followers of Francis Johnson—called Franciscans—

vociferously demanded that the Ainsworth group leave the premises, and then took possession of the meeting house, Bruinistengange. This was wrong on moral and legal grounds. For a while the dispossessed held meetings in a former synagogue down the street. Johnson, victorious, retained part of his congregation including Daniel Studley, Deacon Bowman, and all the other officers but two, one of whom was Elder Jean de l'Ecluse, recently married to Jacqueline May, elder sister of Dorothy May. In Ainsworth's place, Richard Clyfton was chosen teacher. Later Studley was expelled from the church. In 1616 Richard Clyfton, the Pilgrim's first pastor, died in Amsterdam at the age of 63, a broken-hearted man, separated even from the followers of Francis Johnson.

The Ainsworth group, forced out of the meeting house, removed to nearby Emden and then decided on emigrating to the New World. Embarking on a rickety ship, the best they could afford, many of them met death on tumultuous seas very close to their destination, when the vessel floundered off the Virginia Capes. Francis Johnson died in Amsterdam early in 1618. History is silent on the destiny of his once-attractive wife Thomasine, who had caused such a commotion with her highly fashionable hats and plumes.

Meanwhile John Smyth died in obscurity, succumbing to illness and terrible economic hardship. The records tell of his modest funeral service held in the Great Cake House. Then the remnant of his following took his body carefully to the Niewe Kirk in Amsterdam for burial. His leaderless flock now sought to join another group, and in 1615 were admitted to the local Mennonites. After a while a separate service in English was conducted for them in Jan Munter's bakery, but soon they were absorbed by the Dutch and all traces of them forever lost.

When one considers the circumstances of the era in which he lived, John Smyth was a man far beyond his times. In his later years, as truth came to him in painful revelation, he had the strength of character to withdraw from the rigidities of dogma and the fierce intolerance which it bred. Even the Old Testament warned of being "not righteous over much," which led only to blind zeal, denunciation of family and friends, and petty criticism of the outward forms of the church. In his last publication, printed posthumously in 1612, the year he died, Smyth declared himself apart from all conflict about ceremony and ritual. "It is enough for a man to be penitent and a faithful Christian." He denounced as a "vice" the practice of censuring the conduct of others. Of this, he admitted, he and his brethren had been guilty in their former days in their "preposterous imitation of Christ."

In the final baring of his soul, Smyth courageously declared that if any of his old associates were to charge him with inconstancy, "they could think of me as they please . . . I will every day as my errors shall be discovered confess them and renounce them. I profess I have changed and shall be ready still to change for the better." He was a free man in his conscience when death claimed him. After pain and sorrow, he reached the end at peace with himself and the world, finding his triumph in the assurance of salvation that came from his lately found truth of doctrine. From the distance of time, we can perceive the sheer honesty, integrity and nobility of a gentle human being with a cultivated mind and sense of morality, who had come to grips with his own soul. Unfortunately his contemporaries, Francis Johnson, Richard Clyfton, and even John Robinson, considered Smyth's breast-beating *mea culpa* only as "very sad and woeful" conduct.

While the group settled into working, churching, loving, marrying and having children in Leyden, forces were current which would eventually prevent them from making this their permanent home and lure them thousands of miles away to a New World wilderness. A latent restlessness, and a strong feeling that they were not yet ready to surrender their Englishness and become Dutch, would impel their leaders to seek new solutions.

Chapter 10

DECISION TO LEAVE THE NETHERLANDS

Why did the Pilgrims in Leyden finally decide to go to America? What was the situation in regard to colonization in the New World? When Christopher Columbus returned from his great voyage of discovery in 1492, few people paid attention to his achievement. Europeans went about their business as usual. King Henry VII of England thought so little of John Cabot's discovery of Newfoundland in 1497, he perfunctorily awarded him only the equivalent of $50, and then forgot all about Newfoundland. In France, King Francis I sent Verrazano out on explorations along the American coast, but, like Henry VII, relegated the subject to the back of his mind.

The kings of Spain continued to favor America as a place of colonization, but their attention was directed to South and Central America and the present-day Mexico. Spanish settlements pushed northward until St. Augustine, Florida, was settled in 1565. In England, the truly great work of colonization occurred during the reign of Elizabeth. By mid-16th century there were many stalwarts eager to gain new lands and fortunes for their Queen: Sir Martin Frobisher, Sir John Hawkins, Sir Humphrey Gilbert, Sir Francis Drake and Sir Walter Raleigh.

Those at Leyden were aware of the founding of Jamestown, Virginia, in May 1607, on the James River. The London Company had sent out, under Captain Christopher Newport, three small vessels, the largest of them the 100-ton *Sarah Constant*. She tossed about for four months at sea before reach-

211

ing her destination. They knew about the colonial efforts in New France or Canada, and observed as well the adventures of Captain John Smith. Smith had written about his experiences in and enthusiasm for America in a book titled *A Description of New England,* which appeared in June 1616. In it he revealed his dream of a vast land peopled with free men.

After publication of this book, the Pilgrims discussed the possibility of inviting Captain Smith to Leyden to lecture about the New World in expectation of their settling there. While Captain Smith was perfectly willing, they had little means to provide for his traveling expenses from London and to pay him for his services, so they contented themselves with merely buying his *Description*, which William Bradford read to the congregation at the Thursday evening meetings. Captain Smith remarked bitterly on their penuriousness that they found it "cheaper to buy my book."

The London Company during 1617 became reluctant to engage Captain Smith any further, and he turned again to the Plymouth Company, which, that same year, was superseded by the Council of Plymouth. King James conferred upon its 40 members almost unlimited privileges. They were given all the land in the New World lying between the 40th and 48th parallels of north latitude and extending from ocean to ocean. King James thus granted absolute jurisdiction of more than a million square miles to 40 men. Thenceforward colonization plans were projected in all earnestness, the King appointing John Smith Admiral of New England for life.

The year 1618 found the Pilgrims in Leyden seriously considering whether or not to go to the New World. The younger members generally were in favor of emigrating and the older people against it. As late as the winter of 1617 it still looked as if those living at the Green Gate had found a permanent home. Several of the congregation had become naturalized citizens of Leyden. Many had purchased substantial houses in this Dutch city and marrying continued at a good pace. Young Edward Winslow, who had come from London as assistant to John Reynolds, the printer employed by the Pilgrim Press of William Brewster and Thomas Brewer, fell in love with Elizabeth Barker, formerly of Chester, England, and they were married in Leyden. Likewise, Deacon Samuel Fuller, a widower, married his third and last wife, Bridget Lee.

Underlying the congregation's daily routine of living was their general anxiety for the oppressing poverty in which they found themselves. They were heavily taxed to keep up the church's activities and to pay for the meeting house they had purchased at Green Gate. The wage-earners worked long hours for a bare livelihood, and children were often called upon to help. Babies were being born, but new Separatists were not emigrating from England because of the dim prospects of making a good living in Leyden. Some of the English in Holland had already given up the struggle and returned to their former homes in England, choosing, as Bradford was later to write in his *History*, "the prisons in England rather than this liberty in Holland with these afflictions."

The elders continued to be concerned that their children would be absorbed into the Dutch nation. It was evident to all that the young people liked the free and easy ways of the Dutch, their ready laughter, their will for pleasure. However, their parents took a dim view of Dutch jollity, particularly on Sundays, when the Netherlanders seemed to profane the Sabbath by making of it not a holy day of quiet and prayer but a joyous holiday. The young people's doings surely vexed their English parents, but was it not also the eternal gap between the generations? Pastor John Robinson was amused to find in a book at the University of Leyden a passage which seemed to epitomize the very conduct of the English youngsters: "Our youth now love luxury. They have bad manners, contempt for authority, disrespect for older people. Children nowadays are tyrants . . . they contradict their parents, chatter before company, gobble their food, and tyrannize their teachers." The author: Socrates, writing in the fifth century B.C.

At one of the Thursday evening meetings, a woman, elderly enough to express an opinion, arose and protested simply but effectively against leaving Holland. She was philosophic enough to admit that children were alike from one generation to another, and that their conduct in Holland was not so startling. "Outside it is raining very hard tonight," she said softly, "and the streets are glisteningly wet. The tree in front of our meeting house here at Green Gate is weeping tears, and tears are shivering on every leaf and filtering down. The tree is weeping over those among us who yearn to leave our homes here in Leyden and go across the ocean into a wilderness."

They sat on the backless wooden benches for three long hours discussing the contents of a lengthy letter addressed to them by Captain John Smith. Thick blue smoke rose from the men's pipes. Their clothes were damp from walking to the meeting in the downpour. Mugs of beer were passed around but brought little refreshment. At last Elder William Brewster arose and said, "We have thus far agreed, then, that it is not necessary for Captain Smith himself to come here to Leyden, that his books and maps will suffice to teach us."

William Bradford could not let the opportunity pass without airing his views. "His book is really fascinating, and I shall be glad to read from it aloud at each of our Thursday evening meetings. We better listen to John Smith and emigrate to the New World right now, because before long the twelve years truce between Holland and Spain will come to an end. All around us dire preparations are under way, making it quite clear that Catholic Spain is determined to stamp out religious freedom in Holland. She has already declared war on Protestant Germany."

"Yes, I concur with Brewster that we had better leave this place," said Deacon Robert Cushman, rising to his feet. All present were most attentive. He had a house in Leyden, five servants and "plentie of richness," so that his opinion would carry some weight. "You know that my friend Myles Standish has assured me that in America we would be privileged to have laws of our own making and live by our own church discipline. I realize the seriousness of the question before us, and that our situation here in Holland is not so immediately precarious—that many of us are, indeed, quite comfortable. But I am in favor, not only of our own church discipline, but of the principle of democracy, too."

At this point, Deacon John Carver's fine voice was raised in assent. Now in his fifties, he was held in great respect, being honest, able and pious. He was the wealthiest man of the group, of stern Puritan reformist principles, adhering as long as possible to the Anglican Church and hesitating to declare himself one of the Separatist radicals vilified by the bishops of England. Carver had prospered as a merchant in Holland and now owned an imposing mansion on Rapenburg, presided over by his charming wife Catherine. The Carvers had not been members of the Scrooby congregation, but were already living in Leyden on the Dark Canal as early as May 1609. However, they had not been identified as members of the congregation at the Green Gate until 1616, when the Carver name began to appear often in the church records. "I, too, am in favor of leaving this place," he said.

Then it was Robert Cushman's turn again. A woolcomber by trade, originally from Canterbury, Cushman was one of the Ancient Brethren of Amsterdam. He withdrew from the flock of Pastor Francis Johnson's church, bought a small house in Nun's Alley, Nonnensteeg, close to St. Peter's in 1611, and in 1612 purchased a bigger house where, four years later, his wife and one of his two children died. He was left a widower with a son, nine-year-old Thomas. In 1617 when almost forty, he married Mary Clarke Singleton, who had come from Sandwich, widow of a Canterbury shoemaker.

"Democracy," said Cushman, "recognizes man's essential dignity. The Dutch fought for it, died for it, and taught us its intrinsic worth. In the New World we could create the Dutch type of democracy as the child of our religion."

"We could have free churches," William Bradford added, "and later we could put a document such as the Dutch Declaration of Independence into practice."

"To choose our own work and our own leaders would be wonderful," Myles Standish added. He was four or five years older than Bradford.

"Apples of gold in a painting of silver," someone called out. It was a young woman's voice, an elegantly pitched voice. Who had been so daring? The women remained motionless and silent.

"She is right," one of the older men said. "Apples of gold in a painting of silver. I don't approve of going to the New World with the idea of becoming our own masters and choosing our own work instead of earning good wages here in Leyden. Those who want to become that democratic will soon find themselves, as the Dutch say, jumping *van de regen in de drop,* from the frying pan into the fire."

"Some of us, though, are facing grinding poverty," William Bradford said. "Some of us have to sit all day in a room weaving cloth."

A man turned around, disdain knitting his brow. "Weaving!" he said. "Weaving of cloth! I hate it. It is for women. I never have become used to it. I am a servant to a Dutchman. I am without my fields, without the horse and cow."

Another man jumped to his feet. "Weaving!" he said. "Women weaving? My wife and my daughter have gotten new Dutch notions. I can't make them weave. All they want to do is cook, clean the house and paint new-fashioned porcelain ware. What do they think I am after all? A rich landowner?"

"In America you could really become one," Edward Winslow offered.

The men looked sceptical. Winslow, who talked easily, came from an upper middle-class family in Worcestershire, an educated young man with means.

"Imagine!" Winslow continued in youthful enthusiasm. "To cross an ocean! To conquer the horizon! To leap under the strange-eyed moon of . . ."

"A round cheese looks better to me than any moon," John Furness said. "But I am a yeoman and I'll admit I love any land. I have land hunger."

"A wilderness is cruel," a quiet-spoken man said. "In that virgin country many of us will surely die from the rape of the land. Mark my words!"

"Not to speak of the Indians," someone else added ominously. The man stood up in terror and edged himself to the wall to lean there limply as his imagination took over. "Those barbarians flaying men alive! It's horrible to think about such dangers."

The women hastily passed around their little boxes of smelling salts as others took up the refrain. "The Indians will kill us!"

"Doom has already befallen many colonists in America."

"We will be all by ourselves in the wilderness without houses, streets or stores—only each other to create everything."

"We will be alone in a forest full of wild creatures."

Confusion reigned as many spoke at once without regard for ordered procedure. Men and women turned to each other and whispered reports they had heard of shocking experiences in the New World. At last Pastor Robinson felt called upon to calm their fears.

"Don't be alarmed," he said gently but firmly. "We have no money with which to go there now, not even if we sold all that we possess. We would have to buy supplies of food, clothing and equipment, beside providing money for passage."

"We could get loans," William Brewster interrupted hastily, fearing the Pastor's words would discourage the enterprise of emigration. "Lately I have been close to the lives of the patriarchs of the Old Testament, which I study more than the scriptures of the Apostles. It is the dream of my heart to return to the simplicity of the faith of those fathers and leaders of their people, even if it means crossing an ocean and beginning life anew in the wilderness."

Now William Bradford arose with the fire of prophecy shining in his young eyes, like Amos, Jeremiah and Ezekiel in the days of yore. "America is the promised land," he said. "It is a good land which has never been conquered by any prince."

"Hear! Hear!" Robert Cushman added. "It is a God-given land, free for the taking by the able and the brave."

Through the uncurtained windows of the meeting house, dusk had already given way to moonless indigo darkness. A thought was now expressed which was uppermost in the minds of the older people.

"My children rarely speak English any more," a man said plaintively. "They go to Dutch schools and speak Dutch to each other, reverting to English only when addressing us, their parents. Imagine, my oldest son has become a Dutch soldier!"

"Yes, yes," someone from the back of the hall said in agreement. "All of our children are becoming Dutchmen and taking the reins in their hands."

"But in the New World that will be corrected," suggested Carver. "You'll see, they will conform again to our ways. In Holland there is simply too much of this freedom. Who wants the young to think for themselves? There is time enough for that when they are fully grown. They are unable to make good decisions without experience, and need our counsel and help."

"As for me, I am through with spending my life indoors," Isaac Allerton said, changing the subject. He had left his tailor shop in London and fled to Leyden before the Scrooby group arrived; later his wife, Mary Norris, joined him. He had become a Dutch citizen. "Before I grow too old, I want to work out of doors where I can see God's sun shine through the branches of an apple tree in bloom. Though I am a tailor, it goes against my religion to make frills for men who curl and wave their hair."

The talk was beginning to become aimless. "We will discuss it further at another time," said Pastor Robinson to avert any hasty, emotionally induced final decision. "If the older ones among us want to go to America along with the young, I'll sail with them as their Pastor. If it turns out that only a portion of our group decides to go, it would be better if Mr. Brewster accompanies them as Elder. Let us therefore have a preliminary vote now."

When the vote was taken in the new way—by ballot—only one-fourth favored sailing across the Atlantic to found a new colony there.

"Let us vote once more," Mr. Brewster suggested. "And in the old way, by a show of hands."

A small number of hands, mostly of the younger members of the group, was raised. William Bradford gallantly controlled his disappointment in the outcome. "Sir Walter Raleigh's book, *The Discovery of Guiana*, is very exciting. It is about a new land in northeast South America, and I'll be very glad to read passages from it aloud at our next Thursday night meeting. Who knows? Perhaps some of us might decide to go there."

"Guiana?" one of the older men asked. "Why in the world would anyone want to go to such a wild-sounding place as that?"

"It lies along the tropical coast of South America, which Sir Walter discovered only 24 years ago, a beautiful country, all rich plains with deer crossing and leaping in every direction, with rolling hills, flowing streams and fruitful groves. He says it cannot be equalled for health and wealth anywhere in the world. The Spaniards even call it El Dorado."

"The Spaniards!" several men cried out in horror. "El Dorado or not, we don't want to come under Roman Catholic Spain ever again."

"Is it really tropical?" Robert Cushman asked with some curiosity.

"Quite—a perpetual summer."

"Then we surely don't want to go there. The heat will destroy our bodies and the softness of living our souls."

No, it was generally agreed, the tropics were not for them. They were not looking for a rich soil and choice fruit without any labor to invest.

Soon thereafter Captain John Smith directed a second letter to Pastor Robinson describing Virginia on the Atlantic Coast of North America as a suitable place for them to settle permanently. However, since the colony was already under the Anglican Church, they felt they would very likely be harassed and persecuted just as they had been in England. However, they continued to consider Virginia as a possibility.

At the following meeting, William Brewster said, "We must begin by establishing our own church and our own government under the immediate direction of our Lord. We will institute the principle expressed in the Dutch Declaration of Independence, that all men are created equal."

"But we'll be under the Church of England, won't we?" a member wanted to know.

"No, indeed," Elder Brewster said with emphasis. "From the beginning we'll practice the Dutch separation of church and state. We'll use their system of local self-government from town meetings up to the highest authority. Like them, we will aim for a president, state governors and senators within a senate."

"Right," William Bradford affirmed. "And we will follow the Dutch written constitution prescribing and limiting the powers of every department of our government. We will see to it that every man may claim his rights under the Dutch land laws and their registration of deeds.

"Will there be schools in this country?" one father inquired.

"We will copy the Dutch school system," Elder Brewster assured him. "In time we will establish free schools for boys and for girls. We will also have a free press."

"Besides that," Robert Cushman added, "we'll practice the Dutch reform of criminal law and the right of counsel for defense, and prison reform as well. We will eventually establish a supreme court like the Dutch, and copy their office of district attorney as soon as we are able to do so."

"Hear! Hear!" a young Pilgrim cried enthusiastically. "Let's start in a new way and in a new country!"

The feeling was contagious, an enchanting, maddening restlessness which infected the younger people especially. Within a few months Captain Smith wrote again, describing further the advantages of settling in Virginia.

Again the subject was brought up for discussion, and someone asked pointedly, "Under whose domain is that area?"

"Under England, the Church of England."

"That will never do, because we want a church of our own."

"The climate is ideal for plantations, and life could be easy there."

"Is it ease we are after? Are not the deeper Christian virtues developed under some hardship?"

The next move was made by the Dutch Merchant Company. They had heard about the Separatists of Leyden wanting to emigrate. Since they needed colonists along the Hudson River, and the Dutch people were reluctant to go, they offered the English free transportation and free cattle. The Pilgrims decided against it. If, they reasoned, we settle along the Hudson River, we will eventually become Dutch, the same as here. We may have freedom of religion, which we already enjoy anyhow, but we will lose our nationality.

The Burgomaster of Leyden now brought forward a new proposition. Some Dutch capitalists would assist them to become farmers in the Netherlands around Middelburg, the capital of the South, where settling permanently would be feasible for them.

"We would be allowed to hold our own church services as we do here in Leyden?" they questioned.

"Naturally!"

It was good to be wanted. At first they were enthusiastic, but in the end decided they could not accept the offer. They would still become Dutch citizens and ultimately lose all traces of their English identity.

The Dutch Trade Company said they would be willing to transport the entire congregation to New Amsterdam on the lower tip of Manhattan, providing furnishings, cattle, and a loan of the funds required. This very generous offer made a deep impression, and the congregation considered it seriously.

"Will you leave our colony to self-management?" they asked in a letter.

"We will," was the reply.

But, against the opposition of many, the congregation rejected the project at their next meeting. Neither Middelburg in the Netherlands, nor New Amsterdam in Manhattan, nor anywhere in the Hudson River district held the right answers for them. These settlements were all Dutch and they were Englishmen, so they politely wrote the Dutch Trade Company, refusing their proposal.

"We are planning a kind of communal society with a common storehouse and with our needs to be taken from a common supply. We will feel ourselves bound and directed in all things by our Leyden Church. All building, planting, trading and governing will be planned for and directed from Holland. But we want to form an English group, speak English and to be English colonial subjects." The letter ended any further negotiations.

The exodus of the Pilgrims from Holland was far different than when they were harried out of England. Then they were beset with persecuting enemies. Their leaders and congregation members were thrown into filthy prisons and denied fair trial. They were betrayed, robbed and cruelly treated. It had taken nearly a whole year of labor and trial to accomplish their first pilgrimage, beginning in the fall of 1607 and continuing into the spring and summer of 1608. A branch of their original church in Lincolnshire under John Smith as Pastor, had gone over to Amsterdam before them without the grim hardships the group from Scrooby would suffer, but the Ancient Brethren had fallen into difficulties among themselves. Pastor Robinson and the Pilgrim church avoided these by removing their numbers to Leyden, after a year's stay in Amsterdam.

John Robinson had been chosen Pastor before there was any thought of departing from England for Holland; his counsel was highly respected and cherished at all times. In deciding to leave Leyden, the Separatists were not beset by enemies. They were settled, many in their own houses, and earned a livelihood in spite of economic hardships. No vanguard had preceded them to the New World, inviting them to join them there, as the Ancient Brethren had done in Holland.

Yet Divine providence for them was always tempered by change and trial. It was as if God was leading them forth out of Egypt into the Promised Land for His own purposes, which as yet were not revealed to them. In the biblical sense, they removed from Rameses and pitched in Succoth, and they departed from Succoth and pitched in Etham. They, too, seemed to hear the voice of Jehovah as he spoke to the Hebrews: "I will take you to me for a people and I will be to you a God and you shall know that I am the Lord your God which bringeth you out from under the burdens of the Egyptians. And I will bring you in unto the land, concerning that which I did swear to give to Abraham, to Isaac and to Jacob, and I will give it to you for an heritage." God awoke within the Pilgrims the great purpose of crossing the unknown ocean, and incited them to it by many inducements, providences, and trials, inward and outward.

It is significant that they were always anxious about losing their English nationality, about being exiles in another land, forever cut off from the language, laws, name and home of Englishmen. They saw clearly that in Holland they were fast coming to this. They wanted a Christian Sabbath, English laws, the English language, English manners and customs, and an English home and education for their children. These thoughts God caused to burn within them.

In that day and age it was something unique in Christianity for this group to experience an inward zeal and great hope, as William Bradford later recalled it, "of laying some good foundation or at least to make some way thereunto for the propagating and advancing the gospel of the kingdom of Christ in those remote parts of the world; yea, though they should be as stepping stones unto others for the performing of so great a work."

They were like the Hebrews of old, whose first idea in getting out of Egypt had been, as it were, simply a three days' journey into the wilderness to sacrifice freely unto their God. However, in retrospect, the Pilgrims do not seem even to have dreamed, while in England, of the great conception of founding a colony for God in the New World. But this was what God intended them to do, and in due time He made it known to them and they became sensible of their missions.

Chapter 11

NEGOTIATIONS FOR PASSAGE

After many discussions, much frank disapproval, and revisions of plans, late in the summer of 1617, two agents were sent to London, Deacon Robert Cushman and Deacon John Carver. They approached the First Virginia Company (or London Company) through Sir Edwin Sandys, son of the Archbishop of York, a patron of the Brewsters when they lived in the old Manor House in Scrooby. Sir Edwin had narrowly escaped being sent to the Tower of London in 1614 when, as a member of Parliament, he was too free in his criticism of James I. Sir Edwin Sandys worked closely with the Governor of the Company, the Earl of Southampton, patron of William Shakespeare. The Company was concerned to recruit colonists for their ventures. The agents from Leyden were required to submit documents that were not in essence averse to the tenets of the Anglican Church.

Certain questions were put to them, which they relayed to the Church in Leyden. In consequence, Pastor Robinson and Elder Brewster drew up a confession of their faith, known as the Seven Articles, which minimized the differences between the creeds of the Separatists and the Anglicans. These were read to the congregation, who found them a statement of submission, whereas Pastor Robinson thought them merely a respectful honoring of the King of England. Many could not make head or tail of the business and were disappointed. "We acknowledge the King's majesty as supreme governor in his dominion," the

225

Articles read. "Obedience in all things is due to him." They were provoked at that, and downright angry at the clause, "We acknowledge the authority of the bishops." But hadn't they fled their country to get away from the power of the bishops? Were they now freely submitting themselves once more to their rule?

After much talk back and forth, Elder Brewster was sent to England with the Seven Articles. Sir Robert Naunton, Secretary of State, was petitioned to present the document to the King. The King himself found no fault with it, but the Privy Council did. Sir John Wolstenholme (or Worssenham as spelled in Governor Bradford's *History*) raised several questions, and the Articles were sent back for revision, arousing real concern at Green Gate.

Robinson and Brewster drew up two statements in which they complained that it "be grevious unto us that such unjust insinuations are made against us." They enclosed the statements in an envelope with a letter addressed to Sabin Staresmore, a Separatist from the Church of England, who was still in London. He later joined the Leyden congregation. One enclosure was rather brief. It held that the Leyden Church was similar to the French Reformed Church, but the second enclosure listed some small dissimilarities. Staresmore himself had no knowledge about the contents of the communications he submitted, since he had not been previously furnished with copies. He was therefore quite ill at ease during the interview with Wolstenholme, and complained later that he certainly wished he had been familiar with the contents, particularly the longer point at which Wolstenholme "stuck so much."

He felt he would have been in a better position, for instance, to reply intelligently to the direct question, "Who shall make them?" when Wolstenholme asked Staresmore about the ordination of ministers and elders. Staresmore said with confidence: "The power, sir, of making is in the Church, to be ordained by the imposition of hands by the fittest instruments that they have. It must be either in the Church or from the Pope, and the Pope is antichrist."

"Ho!" cried Sir John Wolstenholme, "what the Pope holds good, as in the Holy Trinity that we do well to assent to, but we will not enter into that dispute now."

Wolstenholme was to choose which of the two statements submitted by Leyden he would present to the Privy Council, but he decided against either of them, fearing to upset the apple cart.

As Staresmore picked up his hat, and turned toward the door, he said, "What good news have you for me to write to the Leyden people tomorrow?"

"Excellent news, for His Majesty and his Bishops consent."

Unfortunately, the news was not true. James I, indeed, said it was a good and honest motion and even inquired of his minister, "What profits may arise in the parts to which they intend to go?"

"Fishing, Your Majesty."

"So God have my soul, 'tis an honest trade! It was the Apostles' own calling," said the monarch.

But he would not grant permission with the stamp of the Great Seal, and the matter limped along for a year. When Cushman and Carver returned to Leyden, the congregation cooperated with their Pastor in drawing up the Five Reasons, which were more satisfactory than the Seven Articles. In this they said, "We are well weaned from the delicate milk of our mother country . . . We compare well with any company in the world. Industry and frugality are not strange words to us. We are knit in sacred bonds of fellowship, tied to all care of each other's goods."

Accustomed to the freedom taught them in Holland, they considered they would be good colonists in the New World. Like any group of outsiders, the Pilgrims came in for their share of criticism by niggardly Dutch nationals, who envied their sheer ability to get along in a foreign country, and the way their services were sought by employers for "their honestie and diligence."

The church of the Pilgrims, indeed, under Pastor Robinson's care, was so remarkable for peace, brotherly love and quiet industry, that it was publicly noted by the magistrates of the city as a model in those respects. By way of reproof to the jangling of the French church of the Walloons living in Leyden, they said, "These English have lived amongst us now these twelve years and yet we never have had any suit or accusation come against any of them. But your strifes and quarrels are continual."

The Virginia Company was satisfied with the Seven Articles and the Five Reasons. Once more they petitioned Sir Robert Naunton to approach the King, who also was satisfied, but the Archbishop was not. He frowned on the idea that a congregation in an English colony should claim the right to choose or dismiss its clergymen.

"The Pilgrims desire to live under your government and protection," Sir Robert once more told the King. "All they ask is liberty of conscience in that faraway America, and they will do their best to advance Your Majesty's dominions."

Meanwhile, in the fall of 1618, the group of Franciscans— followers of Francis Johnson in Amsterdam—sailed out of Graves End for America, with 200 passengers aboard. Storms drove them far off course. The Captain and other officers died of influenza, leaving no one with the skill to navigate the ship, so they tossed about for six nightmarish months before they finally came to anchor off Jamestown in Virginia. There were only 50 survivors on the ship. It was dreadful news that Deacon Cushman wrote from London, describing the disaster which had befallen the Brethren out of Amsterdam. He wondered how much it would discourage the Leyden people in their determination. Sadly and wisely Cushman wrote, "It doth often trouble me to think that in this business, we are all to learn and none to teach."

Some four weeks later, Deacon Cushman was successful in getting a patent to a tract of land along the northern boundary of the Virginia Colony, in an area between the Delaware and Hudson Rivers. As a precaution, the patent was not taken out in the names of the leaders of the congregation, but in the name of John Wincob of the household of Elizabeth de Clinton, Dowager Duchess of Lincoln. Wincob, a preacher, averred he would go to Virginia with the Leyden people, but changed his mind, and this Wincob Patent was never used. How much worry, pain and money it had cost!

The people in Leyden needed financing for their transportation more than they needed a patent, since the Virginia Company, with which they were dealing had no more funds. The New Netherlands Company promised to provide paid passage and furnish each family with cattle, if the group would settle at New Amsterdam. Since this would mean living in religious freedom, negotiations reached the point that the directors of the company petitioned the Prince of Orange to assign two war ships to convoy them to New Amsterdam. It was deemed fit and proper that Pastor John Robinson, who was well versed in the Dutch language, would lead his flock there, that some 400 families would be induced to emigrate from Holland and England, and that all would be protected from any incursion by King James.

None of this transpired, however, because of the appearance in Leyden of Thomas Weston, a former ironmonger of London. He advised against any further negotiations with the Virginia Company, now almost bankrupt, and with the New Netherlands Company. He asserted that he and his financial backers would assume responsibility for their passage. He was a bold and restless spirit, a man of many schemes, licit and illicit.

"I have come from the Merchant Adventurers of London," he said, standing confidently before them at a meeting, as if the Company, and London, too, belonged to him. "Do not go and meddle with the Dutch or depend upon the Virginia Company.

The 70 adventurers of my company stand ready to help you."
He informed them that the Virginia Company was now bankrupt, and instructed the congregation to draw up a new contract with him, approving the terms of agreement. Then he
returned to London and set about organizing a joint stock company, which was never incorporated, to finance the enterprise.
Two men from Leyden invested, Edward Pickering, merchant, a
member of the congregation since 1612, and Thomas Brewer,
who was then in England. It was an undertaking for profit
rather than religious freedom, and the Leyden people were
considered good workers.

It was decided that a vanguard from Leyden would precede
the others and prepare for their subsequent crossing of the Atlantic. Pastor Robinson would remain behind and Elder Brewster was to accompany this smaller group. Each section would
be *an absolute church in itself*, in view of the dangerous voyage
and separation by such a great distance. Members of one church,
however, would be members of the other, and if the expedition
failed, the survivors would be assisted by those left behind to
return to Leyden safely.

There was never any other formal organization of the
church to be established in America, nor was one necessary. It
was as simple as the growth of two branches from the same vine.
They had the same covenant with the parent church, the same
officers and the same usages. The Pilgrims were to carry from
Leyden into New England that primitive New Testament congregational organization which they had brought from Old
England into Leyden. Their covenant was with Christ and with
one another in him "to walk in all his ways made known, or to
be made known unto them, according to their best endeavors
whatever it cost them." The Church of the Pilgrims on the Mayflower, the First Congregational Church in Plymouth, Massachusetts, in New England, and in all America, dates its
organization from this time.

The Second (Plymouth) Virginia Company petitioned the

Crown for permission to reorganize for the purpose of obtaining title to the northern half of the area within the original Virginia grant, already called New England. Patent was granted for this. However, most of the Leyden people had sold their possessions and invested their money in common stock of the Company of Merchant Adventurers headed by Thomas Weston. Cushman and Carver went to London to deliver the finished draft of the Articles of Agreement and make arrangements for shipping. Everything was to be done in accordance with the contract which Weston had examined and approved.

Weston, for his part, caused bitterness by insisting on amending the contract. The revised agreement now constituted Ten Articles. The settlers were to contribute their labor for seven years, and the investors were to contribute the funds, with all profits placed in the common stock. The settlers were to withdraw supplies of food and clothing as needed. At the end of the seven years, everything would be divided between the settlers and adventurers on the basis of the number of shares held. Each share was rated at a £10 investment. In the final division each settler would also receive a share for every person 16 years of age or older in his household, wife, servants and children. Those ten to 16 were rated at half a share, and those younger were to receive "50 acres of unmanured land."

All of these terms were agreeable to the Pilgrims. What they were angry about was the deletion of two articles from the original contract. One exempted from the final division houses, gardens and home lots. If they knew that eventually these would be their own, they would work hard to improve them in "hours borrowed from our sleep." Also deleted from the amended contract were the two free days in which they could work for themselves. How could they work seven days a week and for a period of seven years? It was inhuman. Still, it was beyond Cushman's discretion to protest, inasmuch as the investors would withdraw their money if the Pilgrims did not acquiesce to these terms, and anyhow there was no time for him to consult the congregation in Leyden. He claimed he had discussed it with Carver, but Carver denied it, saying he was not in London at the time but at Southampton buying supplies for the voyage. Cushman was very much annoyed. He said he wanted no more belated complaints on what he had been able to do in London. "Do you think I have no brains?" he wrote. To his surprise, he received a very prompt reply from Bradford, Winslow, Allerton and Fuller, saying in effect, "Yes, we know you have brains, but you might exercise them in the business."

Pastor Robinson wrote Carver that conditions in Leyden were "very pitiful," since many wanted to ask for their money back. So many, in fact, withdrew from the voyage, that the Adventurers were compelled to recruit other colonists in Leyden who had no connection with the church. This group of additional potential settlers was represented by Christopher Martin, who was to make the arrangements with Cushman and Carver. Born at Great Burstead, Essex, England, he was one of the radical Puritans. Now he was named treasurer for the Company of Adventurers. He suddenly acted like an energetic ball of fire, not bothering to consult much with the other agents in London. Cushman and Weston were upset enough about Carver, who went off to Southampton to purchase supplies he deemed necessary against their express wishes. Now here was Christopher Martin, against the wishes of Cushman now in Leyden, Weston and Carver, running off to Kent to buy supplies which had no place in the acquisition design. He did not even have the grace to tell the others what he was doing. Those in London were writing pressing letters for more money from the people in Leyden. The Company was in dire need of Ł300 to Ł400 to provide passage for 150 people and necessary supplies.

Nevertheless, by June 1620 they were successful in chartering a vessel of 180 tons, the *Mayflower*, and engaged a Mr. Clarke as pilot. He had gone to Virginia the previous year with a cargo of cattle and was familiar with the route. Meanwhile, the group in Leyden bought a 60-ton vessel, the

Speedwell, to transport part of the group to England. Refitted with sails and masts, she was at Delftshaven ready to leave for Southampton.

The Congregation voted that William Bradford go to Amsterdam and try to win others for the plan of emigration through his father-in-law, Mr. Henry May, an elder of the Brethren group in the Ainsworth Church. Bradford took his five-year-old son John along. As a result of his visit, several Brethren signed up. There were now once more a sufficient number willing to sail. But the Brethren of Amsterdam soon reneged. Robert Cushman, furious over their display of bad faith, wrote in a letter: "As for ye groups in Amsterdam, they would as soon have gone to Rome as with us. Our libertie is to them as rat bone and their riggour is to us as ye Spanish inquisitions."

The London Company recruited anyone capable of labor, regardless of religion or even morals. "Our colony won't be like minded. There will be both saints and strangers among us. That spells trouble." There were Stephen Hopkins and his wife Elizabeth, his son Giles and daughter Constantine. Hopkins, who had means and wore good clothes, cared little for the opinions of others. But while his temper was easily aroused, his heart was good and he stood ready to take risks to help others. He worshipped the Lord as he pleased, and defended his right to say so. He had "much knowledge of the Scriptures" and could read and speak well.

In 1609, Hopkins had sailed with Governor Gates to Virginia, but his ship was wrecked at Bermuda. He had signed to serve as assistant preacher to a chaplain after landing in Virginia, but, since he reached Bermuda instead, he considered himself free from his contract and would no longer take orders from the chaplain, the Captain, or even from the Governor. When he declared himself a free man, the Governor termed it treason, and, in the court martial which followed, Hopkins was sentenced to death. However, his biblical condemnation and verbal broadsides scared the Captain, into pleading with the Governor for Hopkins' pardon. After six months' stay in Bermuda, Hopkins returned to England hale and hearty. He signed up for passage on the *Mayflower* with two men servants bound to him, Edward Dotey and Edward Lister, both rough and blustering and looking for a good fight.

John Billington, his wife Ellen and sons John and Francis signed up in London as Separatists, but were not pleasing in the sight of the Leyden people. "One of the profanest families among us," Bradford recalled in his *History* many years later. "I know not by what friends they were shuffled into our company." Some even thought the London Adventurers had appointed John Billington as a spy to report on how their investment was going. He argued, swaggered and blustered, offending and insulting people without restraint or reason, and it was not surprising that his two mischievous, undisciplined sons followed closely in his footsteps. Nor was his wife lacking in impudence and loudness.

A violent temper is often considered a mark of strength among those too ignorant to understand that losing control of one's emotions is in reality a sign of weakness. Many in the group mistakenly prided themselves on their great tempers. Christopher Martin was reported to have the worst temper of all. He was a self-satisfied individual whose rage was instinctive. His face would become contorted with hatred as he filled the air with accusations against whatever hapless person had displeased him. Nevertheless, he was elected to the office of factor, to receive and pay out all money, and as the mediator between the Pilgrims and the Adventurers of the London Virginia Company. Robert Cushman, who had to deal with Christopher Martin in England, wrote the Leyden group on August 17, 1620: "If I call Master Martin for accounts, he insults me with scorn and contempt as if I were not good enough to wipe his shoes. It would break your hearts to see his dealings. Our people complain to me . . . I can do nothing . . . If I speak to him, he flies in my face . . . He calls us waspish and discontented people."

William Mullins, a gentleman who dealt in shoes and boots, living at Surrey near London, signed up to sail with Alice, his second or third wife, a six-year-old son Joseph, and his 18-year-old daughter Priscilla, after investing Ł500 in the enterprise. John Alden, whom Priscilla Mullins later married, was the ship's cooper. According to English maritime law, a ship taking out a cargo of beer must bring back as many beer-cask staves as it sailed away with because of the wood scarcity, and this was the responsibility of the ship's cooper, besides other general repair work. Twenty-one years of age, well-built, tall, blond and blue-eyed, John Alden was warmly welcomed for his graciousness and amiability as a member of the Pilgrim congregation.

In June 1620, the London Company complained bitterly that Cushman and Carver in England were not purchasing enough supplies. What were they to do? Securing more money from the Leyden group seemed almost an impossibility. Some of the women had even sold their best clothes, blankets, cooking utensils, pots and pans to obtain funds. Another letter came in June from Robert Cushman: "We will, with going up and down and wrangling and expostulating, pass over the summer before we will go. To speak the truth, there is fallen already amongst us the flat schism and we are readier to go to dispute than to set forward on a voyage." It would be winter before they arrived in the new country, too late to plant their crops. How could they rely only upon fishing? Trading with the Indians was also an uncertainty. When on June 13 a royal charter was granted to Sir Ferdinando Gorges to settle a colony in New England, he tried to persuade the Pilgrims to join his own enterprise. For 15 years he had doggedly tried without success to establish a New England colony.

It was when someone had made it clear to them that they would need a small vessel for fishing along the New England coast, which could also be used for the voyage to the New World, that the Pilgrims had commissioned Robert Cushman to acquire the best he could find, and thus he bought the *Speedwell*. The English pilot and crew brought her into Rotterdam. An English firm provided the new suit of sails and the new heavy masts and broad spars, against which the Dutch shipbuilders had warned the Pilgrims.

The men put in a store of pork, herring, cheese, eggs, butter, hard biscuits, and "plentie of wine, brandie and ale, leather bottels and drinking horns." In the hold they stored away great heaps of firewood for cooking en route. The women stocked the ship with "skillets and stewing pans to boil the food and plenty of scurvy grass, saltpeter and grated nutmegs and lemon juice to eat with the meat." The men bought a few modern guns, firing with flint and steel instead of the old-fashioned lighted cotton match, some sheets of lead, a keg of powder, a number of broadswords and some big knives.

At long last the expected letter arrived, telling that the London Company had hired a ship called the *Mayflower* of 180 tons burden, 113 feet long and about 26 feet wide. It had two decks, three masts barkrigged, a few guns to fight off pirates, and high superstructures or castles fore and aft, as Cushman described her. Far above-average size, she was a fifth again as large as the three ships, the *Susan Constant*, 100 tons, *God Speed*, 40 tons, and *Discovery*, ten tons, in which Captain John Smith in 1607 sailed to Virginia, and the *Mayflower* was seven times as large as the two small craft, one 15 tons and the other ten, in which Samuel Champlain explored the Gulf of St. Lawrence and the New England coast in 1605.

The *Mayflower* had been engaged since 1616 in the Mediterranean wine trade, and had spent some years hauling fish, timber, turpentine, tar and other strong-smelling products from Norway. On her last trip before embarking with the complement of Pilgrims, in May of 1620, she brought in more than 50 tons of wine from France, and so her hold still reeked from wine. She had a few cabins but depended for sleeping accommodations mostly on rough partitions, bunks and cubbyholes. Nobody knows for certain what she looked like as ship records of that time are meager. Her name was popular; there were about twenty other English vessels called the *Mayflower* registered in 1620.

Shortly after the letter telling about the hiring of the *Mayflower*, a messenger from London arrived at Leyden with the news that the date of departure had been set for July 21, 1620. Pastor John Robinson proclaimed the preceding day a time of fasting. At noon he opened a meeting which lasted the rest of the day. For his last sermon, Robinson chose as his text, Ezra, Chapter 8, Verse 21: "And there at the River Ahava, I proclaimed a fast, that we might humble ourselves before our God and seek of Him a right way for us and for all our children and all our substance." The rest of the time, wrote Bradford in recollection, "we spent in pouring out prayers mixed with abundance of tears." All were loath to leave "ye goodlie and pleasant citie and tears gushed from every eye." They comforted themselves in becoming "ye stepping stone for ye religious settlement in America . . . Then we refreshed ourselves with making joyfull melodie in ye hearts as well as with ye voices." Many among them were expert singers, and the Psalms were sung to comfort their souls and give them spiritual strength.

At sunrise on July 21, 1620, the hour of leaving had come. The day was sweet with the smell of Holland's full summer. Forty-six people were to go of the 300 souls at the Green Gate, half of them children. Brewster, Cushman and Carver were still in England occupied with the arrangements for passage. Only Mr. and Mrs. Brewster and William Bradford came from the original congregation of Scrooby's Manor House. With the exception of Brewster, a patriarch of 60, Isaac Allerton, the tailor, was the oldest of the group at 36. His wife, Mary, who was pregnant, brought their three children with her, the youngest, Mary, only two years old. Mary Cushman and her small stepson Thomas would meet her husband in England, as would Catherine Carver. Mrs. Carver brought her maid servant, Desire Winter, and a man servant. Mary Brewster would meet her husband at Southampton, where he would slip away from the Bishops' authorities and board the *Speedwell.* She brought her two youngest sons, Wrestling (with the devil) and Love (of God). She left behind her teenage daughter Fear and Patience, now 20, who were staying with her son Jonathan, recently widowed at the age of 27, his wife apparently dying in child-birth, and the baby soon after. There were also William and Dorothy May Bradford, who decided to leave their five-year-old son John with the Robinsons. So great was the hysteria and anguish of the little boy on being parted from his parents, especially from his young mother, whom he was destined never to see again, that he clung to her desperately, screaming for her not to leave him. Some writers believe this tragic farewell had something to do with heartbroken Dorothy's mysterious death a few months later after arrival in Massachusetts. When John was twelve he was reunited with his father at Plymouth Plantation.

Also in the group were William White, woolcomber, and his pregnant wife Susanna Fuller, with their three-year-old boy Resolved hanging on to her skirts. And there were Deacon Samuel Fuller, physician and surgeon, and his wife Bridget Lee, whom he married in 1617, Agnes Carpenter, whom he married in 1613 having died. Francis Cooke, woolcomber, left his wife in Leyden, but took his young son John with him. John Turner, merchant and citizen of Leyden, brought his two sons, both of whom would die by 1621. Thomas Rogers, camlet merchant and citizen of Leyden, brought his son.

John Crackston took his son John. This unfortunate boy was to become lost in the woods near Plymouth Plantation, his feet frozen, and die of gangrene in 1628. There were also Degory Priest, the hatter, Moses Fletcher, a blacksmith, and young John Goodman, who had been married only a few months previously.

When ready to board the canal-boat that would tow them to the coast, Pastor Robinson once more led them in prayer, all crying out with him. They took their sad leave with mutual embraces and reassurances, although they knew full well they would never meet again unless God were willing. The horseman blew his horn, the horses on the tow path strained forward, and the canal-boat glided on its way. Besides Pastor Robinson, many of the Leyden congregation and some from Amsterdam, 50 miles away, came to see them off. It was 14 miles from Leyden to Delftshaven on the coast, where their vessel, the *Speedwell,* lay at anchor at the wharf. The Pilgrims enjoyed their last view of the Dutch landscape, the wide, level plain, the farm houses and stately mansions with their gilt-spiked iron fences, and cattle grazing knee deep in the incredibly luscious green grass. They glided past many gardens, now gay with blooming roses, marigolds, larkspur, Sweet William and pansies, but the tulips had finished their blooming.

The canal-boat bypassed The Hague and was towed parallel with the highway to Delft. From there, it was a straight course to the coast. From one set of sluice gates to another, they were actually lifted above the land level until they finally reached the sea level of their waiting ship. The ancient town of Delftshaven, dating back to the year 600, with its twisting waterways and tangled streets, lay in Rotterdam's western district; it was the harbor of Delft until its absorption in 1886. Today there are memorial tablets in the Voorhaven Church, where the Pilgrims worshipped before their departure, and another tablet marks the approximate site of their embarkation. Delftshaven had seen many ships sail, but this was the first time it witnessed the leavetaking of a group of voyagers bound for the New World.

Men, women and children prepared to spend the night at the wharf, after their baggage, food supplies, bundles of bedding and clothing, utensils, and guns had been placed on board.

Few went to sleep, except the little ones, all preferring to stand about in small groups to spend the last precious hours in Europe with their friends who had come to say farewell. Lanterns burned throughout the long night, and refreshments were taken as they remained in "prayers, singing and ye Christian discourses." Early on the morning of August 1, Dutch counting, or July 22, English reckoning, a fair wind began to blow; the tide turned favorable and they had to get under sail without any further delay. Pastor Robinson fell to his knees, and all with him on the wharf joined in a last prayer. "Tears now gushed from every eye and sundry Dutch strangers on ye key as ye spectators could not refrain from tears," recalled Bradford. Three volleys of arms and three cannon shots were fired in salute as the *Speedwell* slowly got under way.

The travelers watched the great waves roll toward the coast. They raised the English red cross of St. George in token of their native country, even though some had become citizens of Leyden, Holland. The vessel arrived in Southampton four days later, which was very slow progress. It gave them some misgivings about her seaworthiness for a long voyage.

The *Speedwell* needed more repairs, which meant more delay, and Cushman was wild with impatience as they stumbled into August. The *Mayflower* had been waiting for some days, having sailed from London a week before with the people on board gathered together by the Merchant Adventurers. The two groups introduced themselves to each other and fell into ready talk about many things of mutual interest. Cushman, Carver and Martin were still at odds about the supplies and the amended articles of agreement. Cushman complained that "some Ł700 had been spent here at Southampton upon what I know not." Martin refused to take time out to explain or show a written report. Carver disagreed with both Martin and Cushman for their emotional conduct, but it was Thomas Weston who added the last straw to the camel's back. He came down from London with the amended articles of agreement, and when the leaders of the Leyden group refused to sign upon his peremptory demand, he was "much offended" and said he washed his hands of the entire business, which meant he would not extend another penny to the enterprise. When the harbor master of Southampton demanded £100 for port charges, there was nothing for it but to sell 80 firkins of their precious Dutch butter for £60 and to make up the difference by selling badly-needed swords, muskets, leather and some oil.

Holding a meeting, they elected John Carver Governor of the colony, with William Brewster, William Bradford and Edward Winslow as assistants. Guidance for the formation of their American colony came in a long letter from Pastor Robinson, dated Leyden, July 27, 1620, which repeated most of the precepts in his farewell sermon. Elder Brewster read the letter aloud on the deck of the *Speedwell* to his people. The Pastor's suggestion of a government of the people and by the people came from the Dutch Declaration of Independence, and would become the model for the Mayflower Compact. Robinson urged them "to repent of all of their sins known and unknown . . . to store up patience against ye evil day when we take offence at ye Lord himself in His holy and just works." They were also "to avoid the pursuit of private profit as a deadly plague and direct their efforts to ye general convenience." Above all, he urged, they were to "cultivate peace and harmony with all men especially among themselves."

Chapter 12

PERILOUS VOYAGE

Although they already had experienced delay upon delay, being detained at Southampton was especially nerve-wracking for the voyagers. It culminated a dispiriting sequence of harassments: The Adventurers put them off . . . King James held them up . . . the Archbishop tried to prevent their sailing . . . buying supplies and equipment took weeks . . . incompetence devoured more valuable time.

There were three distinct groups: the Pilgrims from Holland and England; the Puritans, who were discontented members of the Church of England; and the "Strangers," who were either members of the Church of England or indifferent toward religion, but being born Englishmen, never knew any other affiliation. They had been recruited as passengers and settlers by the Merchant Adventurers, who cared little how they prayed. Some of them held themselves aloof from the Pilgrims or even mocked them for their piety. Others submitted to their benign influence and even joined in the church services, feeling their spirits uplifted thereby. The Leyden people were interested in establishing a theocratic colony with ownership of their own land, and wanted to be independent of any master. It meant a break from the stratification of English society, where all rights and privileges lodged in the aristocracy.

Practically all of the Pilgrims were humble people, more country folk than city-bred. Some were middle class, some even well-to-do merchants, who could afford better quarters than the

243

cubbyholes assigned to them, but there was no choice. None were noblemen. Not one signed himself "Gentleman", not one of them was entitled to a coat of arms. Not one had completed a college course which entitled him to be addressed as "Master" or "Mister". William Brewster came closest to it. Only four of the passengers had reached the age of 50; most were in their twenties and thirties and many were children.

It is commonly but mistakenly believed that all on the *Mayflower* were Pilgrims, knit by family and personal ties, that all were from Scrooby by way of Amsterdam and Leyden, and that all burned with zeal to found a church of their own in the wilds of the New World. This is pure myth: only three people are known to have been from the original Scrooby group— William and Mary Brewster and William Bradford. Only 41 people, little more than a third on board, came from Leyden, 17 men, ten women and 14 children. They were not looking for spiritual salvation so much as for economic opportunity, to better the lot of themselves and their children. They had seen the bitterness of poverty, and, as common people, were in revolt against the injustice of invested privileges. There was, indeed, no blue blood on the *Mayflower*.

When the *Speedwell* and *Mayflower* first set sail from England on August 5, 1620, after a further delay of almost two weeks to get the *Speedwell* into condition, the *Mayflower* took the lead just outside port. However, after a few days out, it was obvious that the *Speedwell* was leaking badly. Captains Reynolds of the *Speedwell* and Christopher Jones of the *Mayflower* decided to turn back, and the two vessels put in at Dartmouth. Passengers and crew were very much upset by the *Speedwell*'s latest delay, although the more philosophical were grateful her disability did not show up in mid-ocean. The sailors were incensed against Christopher Martin, acting as governor on the *Mayflower*, for his meddling in things "he knew nothing about." Everyones' nerves were raw. To prevent the desertion by disgusted passengers, Martin confined them below decks and forbade any to go on shore, a miserable punishment.

After a loss of almost two more weeks, the *Speedwell,* with the promise of a better performance, and the *Mayflower* again set sail on August 23. But the evil genie was averse, and after four days out from shore, the *Speedwell* once more began to leak very seriously. As the passengers and crew fretted, more than 300 miles from land, the Captains conferred and decided to turn back again. The *Speedwell* leaked so badly they could scarcely free her of sea water with heavy pumping. Both vessels reset their sails for England and put in at Plymouth. It was baffling that they could find nothing specific the matter with the *Speedwell* but "general weakness". This time the decision had to be to proceed without her. The *Speedwell* returned to London for a complete refitting, proving quite seaworthy afterwards on several profitable voyages. This led Bradford to accuse Captain Reynolds and his crew of faking the leaks, since they had signed a contract to remain in the colony for a year and wanted to break the agreement. This may not have been the case, however, as Bradford himself admitted that the masts placed on her when she was refitted at Delftshaven were top-heavy in the first place.

With the *Speedwell* eliminated, the Pilgrims faced another crisis. Some had to give up the voyage; obviously the *Mayflower* could not take everyone. She had set out with 90 passengers and the *Speedwell* with 30. Some 20 persons had to be left behind, some who were convinced what had befallen was a bad omen, some because they felt their young children presented too great a burden for the Atlantic crossing. Among these were Thomas Blossom, his wife and two sons, who returned to Leyden, and Robert Cushman's friend, William King, who decided he would rather take his chances in Europe than become "meat for ye fishes." Robert Cushman, who had suffered so many arrows of misfortune and had striven so unselfishly for the good of all, decided to drop out for the time being.

Finally, seven weeks after the departure from London, the *Mayflower* headed westward with such a good gale roaring in her rigging that the vessel made six or seven knots an hour. The new sailing date, September 6, 1620, was dangerously late, but they had no other choice. The North Atlantic is cold even in August, as present day ocean travelers well know. By September, the passengers found it almost impossible to keep themselves warm and their clothing dry. They survived on hard tack, dried fish, cheese and beer, with little hot food to comfort them. Many suffered the added horror of seasickness.

The list of passengers was reduced to 104. Of these, 41 were Pilgrims or Saints, Separatists who had accepted the Holy Discipline, and 40 were Strangers. The Leyden group and the English group were almost of equal size. Among the Strangers were Myles Standish, a professional soldier in his mid-thirties, and his wife Rose. Standish never became a member of the church at Plymouth even though it was a theocratic settlement, adhering to his old Roman Catholic faith.

Among the Strangers were James Chilton, a tailor of Canterbury, who was on board the *Mayflower* with his wife and daughter Mary; and Samuel Eaton of Bristol, a ship's carpenter, his wife Sarah and son Samuel, an infant at the breast. The largest family was that of Stephen Hopkins of Worton-under-Edge, Gloucestershire, and, earlier, London, who brought his second wife Elizabeth and three children by his first wife, Giles, 13, Constance, 15, and another whose name is lost to us. At sea, Elizabeth Hopkins gave birth to a boy, appropriately named Oceanus, who only survived until the age of seven.

Richard Warren of London had a large family but left them safely at home when he boarded the *Mayflower*. At Southampton, Gilbert, the younger brother of Edward Winslow, joined the *Mayflower*, as did Peter Brown from Great Burstead, Essex. John Billington, 30, and his wife Ellen came from

London. It was their eight-year-old son Francis who almost blew up the *Mayflower* by shooting off squibs near the powder kegs, and their son John, six years old, who got lost in the woods—and found again—on Cape Cod in 1621.

Five hired hands were under contract for a year. In addition to John Alden, the cooper, there were two seamen and two master mariners, Thomas English, who would be captain of the shallop or long boat which was stored between the *May-flower*'s decks, and John Allerton, not related to the tailor Allerton, hired to return to Leyden and assist in bringing more Pilgrims over. It was a great loss to the venture when these skilled mariners died a few months later.

Another large group was the indentured servants, actually bond slaves, eleven men, one woman and six children. The men were strong, fit to do heavy labor like cutting down trees, hewing timbers, building houses, clearing the fields of stumps, ploughing, tending crops, and gathering in the harvest for their masters. The period of indenture usually ran for seven years without pay, but they were fed, clothed and housed. Most of them were indentured to the Leyden group. John Carver could afford to have four, two sturdy young men for himself, Roger Wilder and John Howland, and a boy and a girl for his wife. The Brewsters had Richard More, a seven-year-old orphan, indentured under auspices of the church and Lord Mayor of London, and living with Thomas Weston when taken for the voyage; and his brother, name unknown. Samuel Fuller's servant, William Butten, 22, of Austerfield, died before land was sighted and was buried at sea. The Winslows had a little girl, Ellen More; Elias Story, a man servant of London, and George Soule, 20, from Eckington, Worcestershire.

Last, but surely not least, were the ship's officers and crew, the latter numbering 30 or more seamen, an unruly, drinking bunch, working under a tough old skipper who swore blood-curdling oaths. Christopher Jones, nearing 40, was a hard-bitten sea-dog from Rotherhithe. His kindly nature was well hidden. The first officer, John Clarke, had been to the New World twice before. On his last voyage, in 1619, he went to Virginia with a load of cattle from Ireland. Bradford's *History* names the other mates as Andrew Williamson, John Parker and Robert Coffin, or Coppin, who was the pilot. Recent scholarship reveals that there was a doctor on board the *Mayflower,* Giles Heale, who later had a good practice in London, but apparently the Pilgrim company preferred the ministrations of their own surgeon and physician, Deacon Samuel Fuller.

By the time October arrived, the *Mayflower* had reached mid-Atlantic and was proceeding as rapidly as she could. The weather was quite satisfactory, but passengers got on each other's nerves in the crowded, odious quarters. They could neither wash properly nor change clothing sufficiently, as it was only possible to launder and hang out a few things at a time. The crew hated the Captain and took to cursing the Pilgrims for their patience and their prayers. One huge bully tormented even the sick, promising to bury them in the briny deep, but by a strange quirk of fortune, he was suddenly stricken and died, and his body consigned to the ocean to the amazement of his fellows, who thereafter "walked better."

The Pilgrims took great comfort in reading and singing the Psalms from their Psalter. These ancient verses offered them the right words for opening their hearts to God. In the history of the people of the Holy Land, they found a similarity to their own dire situation. The Psalms were a guide for their daily conduct, reflecting the entire range of human emotions: sorrow, joy, faith, humility, doubt, hurt, despair, and gratitude to God for His blessings. The Psalms include petitions for help, laments, imprecations and edifications, so that they were guided in responding to crises and danger. From the Psalms they learned how the Hebrew people had called upon God for His aid, how they reacted to joyous events, and how they thanked Him for His bounty. Pastor Robinson had often pointed out how the very first Psalm, *The Two Ways*, presents the kind of life a man designs for himself, seeking and achieving happiness or sinking to the depths of despair. "He will be blessed if he follows the counsel of the righteous, secure like a firmly rooted tree, constantly drawing sustenance from God, but the ways of the wicked are the ways of self destruction and are swept away like chaff before the wind." It is each person who makes the choice. Robinson, Cushman, Carver and Brewster, the guiding lights of the colony, fashioned their character and drew their spiritual strength from the precepts of the Bible, finding in the Scriptures the answer to "Who is a godly man? . . . He who walks with sincerity and uprightly with dignity, with integrity, speaking the truth, doing right, judging all men by their true character rather than by appearances and honoring those who show reverence for God."

They had need for spiritual comfort when fierce winds out of the west brought heavy rainstorms. For days the sailors were unable to put up the suits of sail, and they drifted with bare masts through frightening seas, which threatened to engulf the *Mayflower* and drag her down to an ignominious death with all on board. Many seams in the deck and upper structure gave way under the pounding of the sea, so that water seeped in and soaked the suffering passengers in their bunks and cubbyholes. John Howland, John Carver's man, emerged for a breath of air and was swept overboard, but he was able to grasp onto a topsail halyard trailing in the sea until they pulled him up on deck with a boat hook. Beyond catching almost his death of a cold, he survived. The worst was yet to come. As the storm mounted in its anger, the main beam amidships cracked with a horrifying report. The terrified passengers saw death staring them in the face, but the Captain was in command of the situation. Everyone knew they had left England far too late in the season for a safe crossing, and they recalled with sheer terror the fate which had befallen the Franciscan group of Ancient Brethren from Amsterdam only two years previously.

Even the unbelieving had to think of the awesome power

of prayer when someone miraculously came forward with "a great iron scrue" which the crew was able to use to force the main beam back into place. Then it was secured and held firm with a spare timber braced against the lower deck. At this point the mariners felt the ship was in too dangerous a condition to continue, and the officers pondered the alternatives of proceeding or turning back. Meanwhile Captain Jones, uninfluenced by the excited voices around him, took his time to examine and assess the true strength of his vessel. As the passengers waited breathlessly, many of the children and women weeping unashamedly with fear and misery, Captain Jones said: "This ship is strong and tight under water, even though she may be leaky in her upper works." So breathing a sigh of relief or resignation, they "committed themselves to ye will of God and resolved to proseede."

Howling winds and colder temperatures heralded the coming of November while they were still being tossed about on the bosom of the deep. On November 6, young William Butten, Deacon Fuller's servant, died and was buried in the ocean. Land was sighted on November 10. This date is usually given as November 9, as it appears in Mourt's *Relation*, but has been corrected, since in Bradford's *History* and in the *Relation*, it is recorded that on the day the Pilgrims sighted land, they sailed down the coast until noon, then they turned back and "ye nexte day" tacked around the tip of Cape Cod and dropped anchor in what is now Provincetown Harbor. Later that day they composed and signed the Mayflower Compact, which is dated "at Cape Codd, ye 11 of November." The *Mayflower*, therefore, made its landfall on November 10, unless the Compact is incorrectly dated. It was a great moment when a soft dark line appeared in the distance off the starboard bow, and a sailor in the rigging shouted at the top of his lungs, "Land! Ahoy!" The passengers came running from all sides, crowding the rails and straining their eyes with joy for the welcome sight.

The *Mayflower* sailed to a place off the high bluffs at Truro, but no attempt was made to land. The Pilgrims were seemingly intent on finding a place about Hudson's River for a settlement. They followed the shore until about noon, when they were caught amid breakers and shoals off the present town of Chatham in very dangerous waters. They were relieved when the vessel was brought safely away into the open ocean, where she rested until morning.

The *Mayflower* not only passed through stormy seas, but stormy spirits on board brought the ship to the point of mutiny even as the ship sailed into the harbor. Some bold passengers defiantly claimed that once their feet were planted firmly on shore, they would "use their own libertie for none had power to command them, the patent they had being for Virginia and not for New-England, which belonged to another government with which ye Virginia Company had nothing to do."

There were mutinous speeches and postures by the rebellious, which even continued after settlement at Plymouth until put down by the Governor. Bradford did not include the rebels' names in his *History*, vaguely dismissing them as "some of the Strangers." From other sources we know that in 1609, a group of emigrants left England for Virginia in a fleet of nine ships under the command of Sir George Somers and Sir William Gates, appointed Governor of the Colony, but a great hurricane scattered the vessels. Months afterwards, some of the ships, almost sinking, limped into the Chesapeake and dropped anchor off Jamestown. The *Sea Venture*, the Admiral's flagship, foundered off Bermuda, but no lives were lost. Sir William Gates and Sir George Somers gave the order for the survivors of the crew to build pinnaces to take the company to Virginia. But they grumbled and resisted the order, fearing they would be detained in Virginia by authority of the Commander and their whole lives given to serve "the turns of the Adventurers with their travailes and labours."

A man in the very household of Governor Gates proved

to be the prime instigator of evil. He was a clerk brought along to read the Psalms and chapters of the Bible on Sundays, "a fellow who had much knowledge of the Scriptures and could reason well therein." It was he who, carefully at first and then more openly, began to "advance substantial arguments both civil and divine, falsely quoting the Scriptures, that it was no breach of honesty, conscience nor religion to decline from the obedience of the Governor or to refuse to go further . . . since the authority ceased when the wreck was committed and with it they were all then freed from the government of any man."

This is exactly what some of the passengers argued on the *Mayflower*. The clerk ten years earlier went from sedition to treason and began to preach an organized resistance. This was too much for the authorities, who promptly seized him and brought him before a court-martial on a charge of mutiny and rebellion. He and three or four others were convicted and sentenced to death, and all were executed with the exception of the leader. He succeeded in being pardoned because he "made so much moan, alleging the ruin of his wife and children in his trespass," and quoted Scripture so fulsomely, he overwhelmed the resistance of his judges.

This leader's name was Stephen Hopkins. There is sufficient evidence to substantiate that this was the same Hopkins on board the *Mayflower*, who had previously been to the New World. Since the days of the rebellion in Bermuda, Hopkins had risen to be a master himself, with indentured servants, and would hardly have agreed with those desiring "libertie." Most of the men in the company were goodmen, or the poorer freemen, and servants. Edward Dotey and Edward Leister, the bold young men who were Hopkins' servants, listened to the argument that "here in New England none had power to command them." But we cannot say for certain that these two hotheads were leaders of the mutiny brewing on board the *Mayflower*.

To meet the tense situation stirring, there could, as in the past, be only one thing on which to rely, and that was the written Word. So the Pilgrims drafted a document which would be binding upon all, and the church covenants served as a pattern. William Brewster, who had been Postmaster at Scrooby Manor and was familiar with legal diction, doubtlessly was the writer. As soon as the document was finished, the Pilgrim group assembled in the cabin of the Captain on the poop deck, or at least so many artists have assumed in depicting the historic reading, and thus the Mayflower Compact came into being:

"In ye name of God, Amen . . . We whose names are underwritten, the loyall subjects of our dread soveraigne Lord, King James . . . do by these presents solemnly and mutually in ye presence of God and of one another, covenant and combine ourselves together into a civil body politick . . . and by vertue hereof to enacte, constitute, and frame such just and equall lawes, ordinances, acts, constitutions and offices from time to time as shall be thought most meet and convenient for ye general good of ye Colonie unto which we promise all due submission and obedience."

Those who used the title of "Master" or "Mr." signed first, of whom there were twelve. John Carver placed his signature first, followed by Bradford, Winslow, Brewster and Allerton. Then came Standish, Deacon Fuller, Christopher Martin, William Mullins, William White, Richard Warren and Stephen Hopkins. Twenty-seven "goodmen" volunteered to sign, and a few of the servants, Edward Dotey, Edward Leister and two more.

It was a step forward from feudalism and the system of power and privilege for the aristocratic few. But this revolutionary document, found and preserved from oblivion by John Quincy Adams in 1802, was not the foundation of American democracy. It was a means to maintain conditions on the *Mayflower* against revolt, and to indicate to inferior people in general, and especially servants, their proper place which, was under the control of their masters. Democracy was to be born much later on the fighting frontier of the colonies.

Under the Compact, the *Mayflower* passengers chose a Governor, John Carver, by election, as they were accustomed to do in church matters. The Compact served well as a warning to the discontented to behave themselves, and only after it was duly signed was anyone granted permission to leave the ship. The Compact was in effect for all, even those who had not signed. A crisis had been met and conquered, not by might, but by reasoning, with God's ever-present help. The Pilgrims placed their confidence in the respectability of a written document sensibly arrived at.

Chapter 13

TRADING THE MAYFLOWER
FOR SOLID LAND

At dawn on November 11, Captain Jones maneuvered the *Mayflower* around the tip of Cape Cod, named by Bartholomew Gosnold, into what is now called Provincetown Harbor, spacious and magnificent in its natural protection to ships. They dropped anchor at long last, 66 days out of Plymouth, England, 98 out of Southampton, and almost four months from Delfthaven in Holland. After the Compact was signed and a first party of 16 men sent ashore to bring back wood and water and report on the area, on Monday, November 13, many of the women went on shore with great piles of soiled clothes to wash them at long last.

There was another serious problem. The seams of the shallop or long boat, which had been stored between the *Mayflower*'s decks, were open from rough weather and from the crew using it to sleep in. Repair work began under the direction of Francis Eaton, the ship's carpenter from Bristol. On November 14 and 15, a scouting party roamed the beaches for seafood and found, to their delight, soft-shell clams and what they then called quahogs, later known as the famous cherrystone clams of New England. The big, fat mussels, however, which looked so luscious, made the people very sick.

Not surprisingly, the weather threatened snow with a raw chill which reached into the bones. The building of shelter was of utmost importance. The Captain and crew of the *Mayflower* were very anxious to be rid of responsibility for the passengers

255

before all their provender was consumed, leaving them stranded in the New England wilds. Sixteen men volunteered to explore a river which flowed into the bay, under Captain Myles Standish, whose name now appears for the first time in the Pilgrim record kept by William Bradford. With Standish went Bradford, Stephen Hopkins and Edward Tilley.

During their search, the men came upon mounds of sand. Digging down, they discovered it was an Indian burial spot. Then they found a place with similar mounds, but when they dug in, they happily uncovered baskets of corn and a familiar-looking large European iron kettle with a wire handle. They logically filled the kettle with the corn, which had been scraped away from the cobs, and tried to lug their find back to the ship. This was too burdensome, and they finally discarded the heavy kettle, managing to salvage the corn they had taken from what they called Corn Hill. After three days, they returned, tired and hungry, to those waiting on the *Mayflower* for their report.

"Ah, 'tis a good omen that the Lord has provided us with seed corn for planting in the spring," said a man, his eyes brightening with hope and trust.

"Yes," responded William Bradford wryly, "but we had to do wrong in taking it from the Indians, the rightful owners, and may the Lord forgive us our transgressions."

Truly were the Pilgrims blessed with the patience of Job. Another agonizing delay of ten days followed to complete repair of the shallop, which was at long last declared strong and seaworthy. A second scouting trip was organized to Truro, and the shallop carried 24 passengers and nine of the crew. The long boat was honored in being under the command of Captain Jones, who was very anxious to see for himself what the prospects were for discharging his passengers. They turned out to be bleak. Foul weather forced Jones to turn the shallop back after the 24 passengers got out and determinedly waded to the beach in icy waters up to their hips. Adding to their discomfort, the damp, bone-chilling weather was the forerunner of snow, which fell first in large flakes, but as the temperature dropped, in smaller flakes which did not melt. It was now that many of the men contracted the heavy colds which were to prove fatal in some cases. When the winds died down the next morning, the shallop returned and brought them all to the Panet River. This was the only estuary, and it was far too shallow to accommodate a deep-drawing ship.

More time elapsed, to everyone's misery. Then, on December 6, with Robert Coffin handling the tiller of the shallop and 18 men on the long oars, they rounded the bay and came into Plymouth Harbor, as it had been aptly named by Captain John Smith six years previously. On board the shallop were Edward and John Tilley, Bradford, Winslow, John Carver, his servant John Howland, Myles Standish, Richard Warren, Stephen Hopkins, and his servant Edward Dotey. The cold was unmerciful. The icy sea spray froze their clothing into stiff boards and cut into their faces, although they covered their mouths and chins with woolen scarves and pulled down their caps and hats as far over their foreheads as possible. They looked like hoary old men, the white, fluffy snowflakes clinging to their garments and their unshaven faces. It was almost too much for human endurance; in fact, Edward Tilley and the master gunner fainted during the passage, just as the boat glided past Corn Hill and came into Wellfleet Bay.

First Officer Clarke bravely went on shore and managed to start a fire with flints while the others remained in the boat. Then the men followed and managed to catch some sleep during the night. In the morning they looked around and found they were on an island in Plymouth Harbor, which they named Clark's Island for the First Officer. The *History* records all its dates in the old style, as Britain and her colonies did not shift from the Julian to the Gregorian calendar until 1752. So it was on Tuesday, December 12 (new style December 22) that the group of explorers returned to the *Mayflower*.

The passengers left behind on the *Mayflower* tried to keep themselves occupied, as they waited desperately for the day when they would be once more on solid land to begin a new life. Even a wilderness habitation would be preferable to the hopelessness of continued shipboard existence. Many were ill and depressed. The day after the departure of the exploring party, which included Bradford, his young wife Dorothy fell from the deck into the sea and was drowned. Mystery still surrounds her death, as there is nothing explanatory in the record except what her husband put into his little notebook: "December 7, 1620, Dorothy, wife of William Bradford died." Did Dorothy take her own life? Suicide was regarded in the Holy Discipline as the worst of human crimes. If the distraught girl desperately leaped into the freezing waters to end her misery, this would account for the terse dismissal she receives in the *History* written by her husband. He never mentioned her again. Born in 1597, and married in Leyden in 1613, Dorothy was 23 when she died. Her son John, the Bradfords' only child, who was five at the time, had been left behind in Holland. John did not rejoin his father until 1627. At 25 he married Martha Bourne, who remained childless. In 1645 they moved to Duxbury, then to Marshfield in 1653, finally to Norwich, Connecticut. John Bradford lived until he was 63.

It is little wonder if young Dorothy May Bradford did decide to take her life, when we consider what women were called upon to endure under the hideous wilderness conditions. After the incident of her death and the return of the scouting party, three days of discussion ensued before a decision was reached to head for Plymouth, where it was found the *Mayflower* could not be worked into the harbor because of an adverse wind. Another attempt was made the next day by Captain Jones, and he was successful in getting the ship beyond Clark's Island. Now it was Saturday, and the Pilgrims had to pause in their endeavors to make proper preparations for the Sabbath.

Would there ever be a settlement? Robert Cushman had said hopelessly during his arduous negotiations for passage to the New World: "Friend, if ever we make a plantation, God works a miracle." All agreed that Thievish Harbor, although shallow, was well-protected from heavy winds and was surrounded by woods, so early on Monday, December 18, a party was sent on shore, again pushing off in the shallop under Captain Jones. They directed the boat toward the lower part of the harbor, putting into the mouth of a large brook which emptied into the bay. The banks were steep and led gently up to clearings on both sides of the running water. The party looked around and then decided to walk some seven or eight miles up the beach along the woods' edge. The soil was rich and there were many fine trees: pine, walnut, beech, ash, birch, hazel and sassafras, the latter recognized as a valuable curative. There were also watercress, leeks, onions, raspberries, strawberries, sorrel, yarrow and liverwort, all recognized by the plants rather than the blooms, as it was now deep winter. The group went ashore again the next day and inspected the upper part of the harbor, where they had seen a large stream like a tidal inlet. They followed it for several miles, and named the river the Jones, in honor of the able Captain of the *Mayflower*.

There was further discussion and a vote. Some preferred the new spot they found; others, Clark's Island. Finally they had to call on God "for direction", and resolved to "go presently ashore again" and take one more look at the most suitable locations they had found. Then they took a vote, for in one thing they were in complete agreement: They could not devote any further time to "search or consideration, our victuals being much spent, especially our beer and it now being the 20th of December".

They had come to their destination in the New World, but not before more than six weeks elapsed since the *Mayflower* first dropped anchor on the Atlantic Coast, six weeks of exploring, searching, suffering. Now they unanimously decided to begin their plantation on the high ground along the stream in the southern part of the harbor. This was just behind the boulder which came to be known as Plymouth Rock. There was some cleared land, and fish were plentiful. Later that day, 20 men came in to stay the night, "resolving in the morning to come all ashore and build houses."

But this plan could not be advanced, for a great storm suddenly caught and drenched the men before they had time to erect shelter, and in the morning the waters of the bay were very rough. It was mid-day before the shallop could reach them with food, and the gales were screaming. The shallop was pulled up on the beach and could not return to the ship either that day or the next.

The *Mayflower* leapt about in the gigantic waves, straining at her anchor, as if in rage that she could not better serve her ill-fated passengers. In the midst of the screeching winds, Mary Allerton's labor pains increased as she reached her term. Deacon Fuller, her husband Isaac, and friends rendered what comfort they could, and somehow she was delivered of a fine son, but without the breath of life—"dead born." More pain, more tears, the burial of a small body at sea, and then it was Saturday, when preparations went forward for the Sabbath.

Monday came, December 25, 1620, but the date was disregarded by the Pilgrims who, with the Puritans, said Christmas was an invention of the Pope. John Robinson, their pastor, had found much fault with the Dutch celebration of Christmas and Easter. In his published work, *Just and Necessarie Apologie,* Robinson stated he was certain the Savior was not born on December 25, and besides, why not celebrate His circumcision rather than His birth? So on this day, those able to work went on shore and put down the foundations of the Common House at a site on the north bank of the brook just above the beach. They also put up some temporary shelters for the men who would remain on shore. These were huts resembling a cone made of branches and turf, like those of charcoal burners in

England. The workers posted a guard for the night and returned to the *Mayflower*. As luck would have it, it was on Christmas Day that they were finally reduced to "drinking water," a great hardship for any European. However, Captain Jones provided some old-fashioned Yuletide cheer on board by breaking out a barrel of the ship's scanty supply of beer and inviting the Pilgrims to share the joy with him and his crew.

Those left on shore suffered from the wind, storm and rain which raged all the following day. It was the season of the rains, and the story repeats this sad theme, "very wet and rainy . . . foul weather." The ship lay at least a mile and a half away because she could not be safely anchored closer to the shore, so a great deal of time was lost in going back and forth. A short central street was laid out along the high north bank of Town Brook, which eventually was known as Leyden Street. It went sharply up from the beach and then to the foot of a steep hill, soon named Fort Hill, where Captain Standish established his arms. The lots were eight feet wide and 48 feet deep. There were 19 households; the single men and those widowed or without their wives had to join families temporarily. The amount of land granted to each household depended on the family's size, one lot for each man, woman and child. There was no permanent title; the assignments were just an expediency. The heads of each household drew lots to see which site each would occupy.

The lot at the foot of the street went to a Stranger, Peter Browne, and the next to William Brewster's household, of which Bradford was a part. Then the street was crossed by a road which followed the brook's bank on one side and the clearing on the other side. Above this road, which became Main Street, were the lots of John Billington, Isaac Allerton, Francis Cooke, and Edward Winslow.

The work progressed, but more obstacles were to be put in the way. On January 14, 1621, a fire broke out in the Common House, with much loss of clothing. This especially distressed the sick, who were bedded down on the floor, including Carver and Bradford. On January 21 the entire *Mayflower* company came on shore for the first time for an hour or two to enjoy Sabbath religious services under Ruling Elder Brewster in the Common House, which was about 20 feet square. But this did not mean they had evacuated the ship. That was a slow operation. In a way, the *Mayflower* was still their home. Not until March 21, 1621, four months after the first scouting party came on shore and eight months since the departure from Leyden, did the last of the Pilgrims forsake the *Mayflower* forever in exchange for the stable earth.

They were greatly hampered by the winter and by illness. A scourge struck the Pilgrims, which was a combination of scurvy, from lack of fresh vegetables and generally poor diet, pneumonia and tuberculosis, brought upon the victims by exposure, over-work and lack of sanitation. They paid with their lives for removal to these shores.

On December 24, Solomon Martin died, the sixth and last within that month. On January 20, Rose Standish, wife of Myles, died, bringing to eight the number who expired in January. In February there was a greater loss—17 souls, among them William White, William Mullins and Mrs. Isaac Allerton. Thirteen died in March. Elizabeth, wife of Edward Winslow, died on March 24, three days after the final withdrawal from the *Mayflower*'s hold.

Within three months, half of the company had died, scarcely fifty remaining, and those so depleted physically they were barely able to bury their dead. The scourge also struck hard among the *Mayflower*'s crew, taking half of the mariners, three mates, the master gunner, the bosun and the ship's cook. The bosun was a proud young man who cursed the passengers, but they returned kindness for his cruelty until his heart was softened, and he confessed on his deathbed: "Oh, you, I now see, shew your love like Christians indeed one to another but we let one another lie and dye like dogs." So little did the

Pilgrims think of the ship's doctor, Giles Heale, preferring Deacon Samuel Fuller's ministrations, that no mention of his presence on the *Mayflower* came to light until 1889.

Christopher Martin, the treasurer, succumbed, and only five of 18 wives survived. Only three married couples were alive after the epidemic had run its course. Death claimed many single men, hired hands and servants, ten surviving out of 29. Only the horrible Billingtons escaped without death. At one time, there were a mere six or seven persons to help the sick, at risk of their own health and lives, nursing and caring for them, washing their clothes and providing food and what comfort they could. Of these stalwarts, William Brewster and Myles Standish were tireless, giving fully of their strength and spirit.

Yet they did not deny God nor forsake Him, knowing still that their salvation lay in His help; and somehow the original company survived and grew in numbers. They had planted in the New World a beachhead for the millions who were to follow. They were cut off from their native land and from Holland. There was no aid nor succour in sight. Sadly they watched the *Mayflower* sail on April 5, 1621, their last link with Europe. They lined the beach and waved their farewells, weeping like children as the vessel was brought around, then tacked out of the harbor never to return to these shores.

PASSENGERS ON THE MAYFLOWER

The 180-ton *Mayflower*, commanded by Master Christopher Jones, departed from London in mid-July of 1620 and dropped anchor off the tip of Cape Cod, Massachusetts, on November 11, Old Style, with 102 passengers, including Oceanus Hopkins, born at sea.

The Saints were those who belonged to the church in Amsterdam and Leyden, Holland, after its separation from the Church of England. These numbered 17 men, ten women and 14 children as follows:

Allerton, Master Isaac (c. 1586-1659), tailor of London.
>   *Mrs. Mary (Morris)* (c. 1588-1621), married in Leyden 1611. Died in Plymouth harbor a few days after being delivered of a still-born infant at the height of a winter storm.
>   *Bartholomew* (c. 1612-?), returned to England and became a minister there.
>   *Remember* (c. 1614-1655), married c. 1633 to Moses Maverick, pastor of Marblehead; they had six children.
>   *Mary* (c. 1616-1699), married c. 1635 to Thomas Cushman and became last survivor of *Mayflower* company; they had four children.
Bradford, Master William (1589-1657) of Austerfield, Yorks. Became foster son of William Brewster c. 1602; citizen of

265

Leyden, 1612. Governor or Assistant Governor of Plymouth 1621-1657.

Mrs. Dorothy (May) (1597-1620) of Wisbeach, Cambridgeshire, daughter of Henry May, elder of Ancient Brethren. Married William in Leyden, 1613. Drowned while *Mayflower* was at anchor off Cape Cod. One child, John.

Brewster, Master William (c. 1566-1643), born in Scrooby or neighborhood. Attended Peterhouse College, Cambridge, 1580-1583, and was in service of Sir William Davison 1583-89. Postmaster and bailiff of Scrooby, 1590-1607, ruling elder 1609-43. Operated the Choir Alley Press, 1616-19.

Mrs. Mary (Wentworth) (c. 1568-1627), said to be daughter of Thomas Wentworth, predecessor of Brewster at Scrooby Manor. Married in Scrooby 1591; had five children. Died in Plymouth.

Love (1611-1650), married Sarah Collier in 1634.

Wrestling (1614-c. 1635).

Carver, John (c. 1566-1621) of Doncaster, Yorks., merchant. Connected with church in Leyden as of 1616. Spent 1617-20 negotiating with Merchant Adventurers and purchasing supplies. Deacon c. 1617-21. Died of exposure to heat of sun suffered while working in cornfields.

Mrs. Catherine (White) (1580-1621) of Sturton le Steeple, eldest sister of Bridget, wife of John Robinson. Married c. 1600. Previous marriage to George Leggett 1596, brought one child Marie, who died early. Catherine died of grief soon after her husband. There were no children.

Minter, Desire (c. 1600-?), in household of Carver, daughter of Thomas Minter of the Green Gate congregation in Leyden. Returned to England about 1625.

Cooke, Francis (1577-1633) from Blythe, Notts. In Amsterdam 1607-9 and in Leyden from 1609-20.

John (1612-1695), married Sarah Warren in 1634.

Crackston, John (?-?) of Colchester.

John, who died in 1628, was the little boy who got lost in the woods, suffered frozen feet and died of gangrene.

Fletcher, Moses (?-?) of Sandwich, married Mrs. Sarah Dingby in 1613.

Fuller, Master Samuel (c. 1585-1633), physician and chirurgeon. Was leader of the seceding Ancient Brethren in 1609. Married Agnes Carpenter in 1613; married Bridget Lee in 1617.

Goodman, John (1595-1621), married Sarah Hooper in Leyden in 1619. Did not bring his wife, only his dogs, a large mastiff bitch and a small spaniel.

Priest, Degory (c. 1580-1621) of London. Married Mrs. Sarah (Allerton) Vincent in Leyden in 1611.

Rogers, Thomas (?-?), camlet merchant.

Joseph (c. 1608-1678), married Hannah and removed to Eastham in 1644; they had seven children.

Tilley, Edward (?-1621), clothmaker of London.

Mrs. Anne (?-1621). They brought along two young cousins: Humility Cooper and Henry Samson.

Tilley, John (?-1621), silk worker of London.

Mrs. Elizabeth (Comyngs) (c. 1585-1621) of St. Andrew Undershaft of London. Married John in London 1605; daughter Elizabeth (1606-1687) once thought by scholars to be daughter of John Carver.

Tinker, John (?-1621), wood sawyer; became a citizen of Leyden in 1617. Had a wife and son who both died in 1621.

Turner, John (?-1621), merchant; became a citizen of Leyden in 1610. Had two sons who died in 1621.

White, Master William (c. 1592-1621), wool carder.

Mrs. Susanna (Fuller) (c. 1594-1680), sister of Deacon Samuel Fuller. Married in Leyden 1612 to William White; in 1621 became second wife of Edward Winslow.

Resolved (c. 1615-1680), their son.

Peregrine (1620-1703), son, born on board the *Mayflower* a month after the arrival, first English child born in this area. Died in his 83rd year and had six children.

Winslow, Master Edward (1595-1655), came from Droitwich, Worcestershire. Assistant printer at Choir Alley Press in Leyden, 1617-19. Married 1621 in Plymouth to Mrs. Susanna (Fuller) White.

Mrs. Elizabeth (Barker) (c. 1597-1621) of Chester or Chatham. Married in Leyden 1618, no children.

The *Strangers*, who were not of the church of Leyden or the Ancient Brethren of Amsterdam, included 17 men, nine women and 14 children as follows:

Billington, John (c. 1590-1630) of London, hanged for murder in 1630.

Mrs. Ellen (c. 1592-?) of London.

Francis (c. 1612-?), married in Plymouth 1634 to Mrs. Christian (Penn) Eaton and had nine children. He died in Yarmouth.

John (c. 1614-c. 1628).

Britteridge, Richard (?-1620).

Browne, Peter (c. 1600-1633) of Great Burstead, Essex. Married in Plymouth 1623 to Mrs. Martha Ford.

Chilton, James (c. 1563-1620) of Canterbury, tailor. Married a woman who died in 1661, name unknown.

Mary (c. 1605-1679), his daughter, married John Winslow in Plymouth in 1624 and removed to Boston in 1655 where she died. Had ten children.

Clarke, Richard (?-1621).

Cooper, Humility (c. 1612-?) of London. A small "cousin" brought on the voyage by the Edward Telleys.

Eaton, Francis (c. 1595-1633) of Bristol, carpenter and ship-wright. Married c. 1622 in Plymouth to his second wife, name unknown.

Mrs. Sarah (c. 1590-1621), had son Samuel (1620-?) who was an infant at breast on arrival in Massachusetts.

Fuller, Edward (?-1621) of Redenhall, Norfolk. Married Mrs. Ann (—) who died in 1621. Samuel was a son of Edward Fuller by previous marriage (c. 1616-1683).

Gardiner, Richard (c. 1600-1621) of Harwich, Essex.

Hopkins, Master Stephen (c. 1585-1644) of Wotton-under-Edge, Gloucestershire.

    Mrs. Elizabeth (?-c. 1640). Stephen's second wife. Giles and Stephen were the children by Hopkins' first wife. Elizabeth bore five children at Plymouth.

    Giles (c. 1607-c. 1690).

    Constance (c. 1605-1677).

    Damaris (c. 1617-c. 1627).

    Oceanus (1620-1626), born on board the *Mayflower*.

Margeson, Edmund (?-1621).

Martin, Master Christopher (c. 1575-1621) of Great Burstead, Essex. Governor of passengers on Mayflower, accompanied by his wife, name unknown, who died in 1621. Martin's stepson, Solomon Prower, died in 1620.

Mullins, Master William (c. 1580-1621), from Dorking, Surrey, with his wife Alice who died in 1621, probably the second or third marriage.

    Priscilla (c. 1602-c. 1685), married John Alden c. 1622 and had nine children.

    Joseph (c. 1614-1621).

Rigdale, John (?-1621) from London and his wife Alice who also died in 1621.

Samson, Henry (?-1684) of London. Married Ann Plummer.

Standish, Captain Myles (c. 1584-1656) of Chroley (?), Lancashire. Married his second wife, Barbara, in Plymouth 1623. Went to England 1626, returned with news of Rev. John Robinson's death. Although a leader of the Pilgrims, did not become a member of the church. First wife, Rose, died in 1621.

Warren, Master Richard (c. 1580-1628), merchant of London.
Williams, Thomas (?-1621) of Yarmouth, Norfolk.
Winslow, Gilbert (1600-?), Edward Winslow's brother. Returned to England c. 1646 and died there.

The *Hired Hands* were numbered at five men:

John Alden (1599-1686) came from Harwich, Essex, and was employed as a cooper. Married Priscilla Mullins c. 1622.
Allerton, John (?-1621), sailor, was hired to return for those left at Leyden.
Ellis, — (?-?), sailor, who was engaged to remain a year in Plymouth but returned on the *Fortune* to England.
English, Thomas (?-1621), sailor; in charge of the *Mayflower*'s shallop.
Trevore, William (?-?), sailor, who returned to England with Ellis and spread a good report of the Plantation established at Plymouth.

The *Servants* numbered eleven men, one woman and six children:

Butten, William (1598-1620) of Austerfield. Died before land was seen and buried at sea. Servant of Fuller.
Carter, Robert (?-1621), servant of Mullins.
Dotey, Edward (c. 1600-1655), from London, servant of Hopkins.
Holbeck, William (?-1621), servant of White.
Hooke, John (?-1621), a boy with the Allertons.
Howland, William (1593-1672) of London, servant of John Carver. Said to have inherited Carver's estate. Married Elizabeth Tilley c. 1624 and had nine children.
Langemore, John (?-1620) with the Martins.
Latham, William (?-1645), came with John Carver. After two

decades at Plymouth was sent back to England, thence to Bahamas where he died of starvation.

Leister, Edward (c. 1600-?) of London, came with Hopkins.

More, Ellen (?-1621), described as a little girl who came with the Mullins family.

More, Richard (c. 1615-1624) of London, came with Brewster as an orphan indentured under auspices of church and Lord Mayor of London.

More, — (?-1621), brother of Richard.

More, Jasper (?-1620), came with John Carver.

Soule, George (c. 1600-1680) from Eckington, Worcestershire, came with the Winslows. Married Mary Becket c. 1627; had seven children. Died in Duxbury.

Story, Elias (?-1621) of London, came with the Winslows.

Thompson, Edward (?-1620), came with the Martins.

Wilder, Roger (?-1621), came with John Carver.

(name unknown), maidservant, listed as coming to attend Catherine Carver. Married and died a year or two after arriving at Plymouth Plantation.

THE MAYFLOWER COMPACT

"In ye name of God, amen. we whose names are under-written, the loyall subjects of our dread soveraigne Lord, King James, by the grace of God, of Great Britaine, Franc & Ireland king, defender of the faith &c., haveing undertaken, for ye glorie of God, and advancemente of the Christian faith, and honor of our king & countrie, a voyage to plant the first colonie in the northerne parts of Virginia, doe by these presents sol-emnly and mutualy in the presence of God, and one of another, covenant and combine ourselves together into a civill body poli-tick, for our better ordering and preservation and furtherence of the ends aforesaid; and by vertue hereof to enacte, constitute and frame such just and equall Laws, ordenances, acts, consti-tutions and offices, from time to time, as shall be thought most meete and convenient for the general good of the colonie, unto which we promise all due submission and obedience. In witness whereof we have hereunto subscribed our names at Cap-Codd the 11 of November in the year of the raigne of our soveraigne lord, King James of England, Franc, and Ireland the eighteenth, and of Scotland the fifty-fourth, AN. Dom. 1620."

John Carver	Myles Standish
William Bradford	John Alden
Edward Winslow	Samuel Fuller
William Brewster	Christopher Martin
Isaac Allerton	William Mullins

William White
Richard Warren
John Howland
Stephen Hopkins
Edward Tilly
John Tilly
Francis Cooke
Thomas Rogers
Thomas Tinker
John Ridgdale
Howard Fuller
John Turner
Francis Eaton
James Chilton
John Crackston
John Billington
Moses Fletcher
John Goodman
Degory Priest
Thomas Williams
Gilbert Winslow
Edmond Margeson
Peter Browne
Richard Britteridge
George Soule
Richard Clarke
Richard Gardiner
John Allerton
Thomas English
Edward Doty
Edward Leister

BIBLIOGRAPHY

There are hundreds of sources for information on the Pilgrims. The following proved helpful in pinpointing their story in relation to the period preceding their voyage on the *Mayflower*, used in preparation of the manuscript.

Adams, James Truslow, *The Founding of New England*, Boston, 1921.

Ainsworth, Henry, *The Book of Psalms Englished both in Prose and Metre*, Amsterdam, 1612.

Ames, Azel, 1845-1908, *The Mayflower and her Log July 15, 1620 to May 6, 1621*, Boston.

Andrews, C.M., *The Fathers of New England*, New Haven, 1919.

Arber, Edward, 1836-1912, *The Story of the Pilgrim Fathers 1606-1623*, London, 1897 (difficulties in Amsterdam), Ward & Downing, 1897, New York.

Baker, George P., *The Pilgrim Spirit: A Pageant*, Tercentenary Celebration at Plymouth, 1920, Boston, 1921.

Banks, Charles Edward, *The English Ancestry and Homes of the Pilgrim Fathers*, Boston, 1929.

—————, *Officers and Crew of the Mayflower*, Proceedings, Mass. Historical Society, Volume LX, pp. 210-22, 1927.

Bell, Margaret, *Women of the Wilderness*, New York, 1938.

Benet, Stephen Vincent, *Western Star*, New York, 1943.

Bradford, William, *Of Plimoth Plantation*, Boston, 1956. Edited 1912 by Worthington Chauncey Ford.

275

————, *Letter Book*, in Series I, Mass. Historical Society Collection, Vols. 3-4, Boston, 1794.

————, *A Dialogue between a young man born in New England and some from Holland and Old England*, 1648, in *Alexander Young's Chronicles of the Pilgrim Fathers*, 1841.

Brown, J. Irwin, *Memories of the Pilgrim Fathers in Holland*, by Leyden Pilgrim Fathers Society, printed by E.J. Brill, Ltd.

Byington, Ezra Hoyt, 1828-1901, *Puritans in England and New England*, 1896, London, S. Low, Marston & Co., 406 p.

Campbell, Douglas, 1839-1893, *The Puritans in Holland, England and America*, 2 vols., Harper & Bros., 1893, N.Y. 1912.

Darrach, Henry, *Bradford Family, 1660-1906*, Philadelphia, 1906.

Dexter, Henry Martyn and Morton, *The England and Holland of the Pilgrims*, Boston, 1905.

Eckhof, Albert, *Three Unknown Documents Concerning the Pilgrim Fathers in Holland 1608-20*, The Hague, 1920.

Gregg, Frank Moody, 1864- , *The Founding of a Nation*, 2 vols. The story of the Pilgrim Fathers, their voyage on the *Mayflower*, their early struggles, hardships and dangers in the beginning, of American democracy as told in Journals of Francis Beaumont, Cavalier, A.H. Clark Co., 1915, Cleveland, Ohio.

Griffin, William Elliot, 1843-1928, *The Influence of the Netherlands in the Making of the English Commonwealth.*

Harris, James Rendel, *Finding of the Mayflower*, London, 1620.

————, *Last of the Mayflower*, Manchester England, 1920.

———— and Jones, Stephen, *The Pilgrim Press* (Choir Alley Press and its publications), Cambridge, 1922.

Johnson, George, *A Discourse of Some Troubles and Excommunication in the Banished English Church at Amsterdam*, 214 pages, only 3 copies extant, in Library of Congress,

Wash., D.C., Trinity College, Cambridge, England, Zion College, London.

Kraus, Michael, *The United States to 1841,* University of Michigan Press, Ann Arbor, 1959.

Macauley, Thomas B., *History of England From the Accession to James II.*

Mansfield, Blanch (McManus), 1869- , *The Voyage of the Mayflower*, E.R. Herrick & Co., 172 pages, New York, 1897.

Morehouse, Prof. Frances, *The Laughter of Puritans,* Proceedings of the Middle States Association of History Teachers, No. 32, 1934. This is the quintessence of all the ignorance and errors in regard to Puritanism.

Motley, John Lothrop, 1814-77, *The Rise of the Dutch Republic,* 5 vols., J.M. Dent & Co., London.

Mourt, G(eorge) or Morton (Authors William Bradford and Edward Winslow), *A Relation or Journal of the Beginnings and Proceedings of the English Plantation settled at Plimouth in New England*, London, 1622. Mourt seems to have had no literary association with it except for writing the preface and giving the book to the press. Cf. Alexander Young in this index.

Noble, Frederick Alphonso, *The Pilgrims*, The Pilgrim Press, Boston, 1907, 483 pp,

—————, *History of the United Netherlands.*

Noyes, E.J.R., *Women of the Mayflower*, Washingtin, 1915.

Patten, E.B., *Isaac Allerton*, Minneapolis, 1908.

Pierce, William, *John Penry*, London, 1723.

Plooij, D., *Pilgrim Fathers from a Dutch Point of View*, New York, 1932.

Plumb, Albert H., *William Brewster of Plymouth*, Boston, 1920.

Powicke, F.J., *Henry Barrow, Separatist,* London, 1900.

—————, *John Robinson*, London, 1920.

Ridpath, John Clark, 1840-1900, *History of the United States,* Volume I, *Epochs of Discovery, Planting and Independence.*

Robinson, John, *Collected Works,* 3 vols., edited by Robert Ashton, London, 1851.

Sawyer, Joseph Dillaway, 1849- , *History of the Pilgrims and Puritans, Ancestry and Descendants*, edited by William Elliot Griffis, Century History Co., 1922, N.Y.C., 3 vols.

Smith, Bradford, *Bradford of Plymouth*, Philadelphia, 1951.

Steele, Ashbel, *Chief of the Pilgrims or Life and Times of William Brewster*, Philadelphia, 1857.

Stoddard, Francis R., *The Truth about the Pilgrims*, New York, 1952.

Usher, Roland, *The Pilgrims and their History*, New York, 1918.

Willison, George Findlay, 1897- , *Saints and Strangers, being the lives of the Pilgrim Fathers and their families with their friends and foes*, Reynal & Hitchcok, New York, 1945.

Winslow, William Copley, 1840-1925, *The Pilgrim Fathers in Holland*, a paper read before the New England Historic Genealogical Society on March 4, 1891. Boston Congregational Sunday School and Publication Society, 1891, 24 p.

Young, Alexander, *Chronicles of the Pilgrim Fathers 1602-25,* Boston, 1841 and 1844. Chronicles of the First Planters of the Massachusetts Bay, Boston, 1846.

Additional Readings

Leidsche Universiteit, Brieven en Papieren van de Pelgrims Stads Documenten

Amsterdam Universiteit, Geschriften over de Pelgrims Kerk Geschiedenis van de Pelgrims

Arber, E., De Geschiedenis van de Pelgrims.

Ds. John Robinson, Leiden Antwoord tot een vriend

Plooy, Harris & J. Rendel, Leidsche Documenten in relatie tot de Pelgrims

INDEX